EX LIBRIS

Mark
~~and~~ Burson

Fishes and Their Ways

Fishes an

Illustrated with photographs and drawings

Their Ways

CLARENCE J. HYLANDER

The Macmillan Company, New York

Collier-Macmillan Limited, London

Marineland of Florida

591
H

Jacket photograph courtesy
Marineland of Florida
Endpaper photograph courtesy
Mozert of Silver Springs
Copyright © Clarence J. Hylander, 1964

Library of Congress catalogue card number: 63–17091

The Macmillan Company, New York
Collier-Macmillan Canada Ltd., Toronto, Ontario

First Printing

Printed in the United States of America

To
BONNIE,
SANDY,
and
SUSIE

A trio of youthful and ardent fishermen

Contents

Darter. *The Sea Bass Family:* White Bass, Yellow Bass, White Perch.

Family: Sandbar Shark, Leopard Shark, Smooth Dogfish, Tiger Shark. *The Spiny Dogfish Shark Family:* Spiny Dogfish, Greenland Shark. *The Skate Family. The Electric Ray Family:* Torpedo. *The Stingray Family. The Manta Family. The Sawfish.*

Foreword

Fishes and Their Ways is a book about the fishes found in
the streams and lakes of the United States and in the seas
bordering its shores. Here a fisherman will meet many old
friends: trout and bass, perch and catfish, bluefish and tarpon.
But he also may widen his acquaintance to include such
strange native fishes as the bowfin and paddlefish, stickleback
and mosquito fish, anglerfish and triggerfish. This is more
than a get-acquainted book; it is as well an invitation to
explore one of our few remaining frontiers—the realm of
underwater life. The recognition of fishes by name and
understanding of why fishes look and behave the way they do
are a common meeting ground of fisherman and naturalist
alike.

Fishes are significant in many ways. Of all the forms of
wildlife they are by far the greatest single source of food.
Fisheries provide much of the human diet in many parts of
the world. Fishes also play a key role in recreation: fishing
ranks as the nation's number one outdoor sport. Millions of
men and women of all ages spend countless hours pursuing
elusive game fishes. Other fishes, because of their appearance
or interesting habits, are popular as aquarium animals,
bringing a new kind of nature into our homes. But even if

one is not interested in fishes for these reasons, he cannot fail to be intrigued by their way of life. Until recently one had to be content with being an outsider, peering into the world of fishes from the surface of the water. The advent of scuba diving and the use of snorkel tubes have changed all this. Underwater exploration is now possible for anyone who wants to meet fishes face-to-face in their own element. Fish watching is becoming as popular as bird watching.

For centuries man has lived along the shores of the under-water realm, skimmed its surface, hauled a wealth of food from its depths, and fished the game species for sport. Until recently very little was known of the private lives of fishes, the animals that dominate this realm. But modern scientific developments have opened new underwater vistas. We have diving vehicles capable of exploring the ocean bottom, electronic devices to measure the movements and habits of fishes, improved underwater techniques, and specially equipped vessels for studying oceanography (the science of the sea) and limnology (the science of fresh waters). Apart from any practical applications, fishes are interesting to biologists because they reveal such perfect adaptation to life in the water. All life began in the water, and fishes existed in this environment before there were any land vertebrates. They have had a long time to evolve into their present form with bodies and activities suited to the great variety of habitats found in the water.

Fishes and Their Ways, like other volumes in the "Young Naturalist Series" * is an introduction to one of the biological sciences. In this book the science is ichthyology, the study of fish life. Nature study is a rewarding hobby, but when it is also a phase of biology it opens a door into an

* Previously published titles in the "Young Naturalist Series" include: *Sea and Shore,* a freshwater and marine biology exclusive of fishes; *Trees and Trails,* a forest biology; *Animals in Armor,* an introduction to herpetology; *Animals in Fur,* an introduction to mammalogy; *Insects on Parade,* a beginner's entomology; and *Flowers of Field and Forest,* an introduction to the ecology of flowering plants.

exciting world where observation, research, and experimentation contribute to a better understanding of living things. The first two chapters of our story deal with fishes as a group: their appearance, structure, and activities. They answer many questions that may already have come to your mind when you admired the sleek streamlining of the salmon in your net or observed a pickerel amid the water weeds of a pond. Why are fishes covered with scales? Why do swift-swimming fishes have forked tail fins? How does a fish swim? Why does a fish have fins? Why are many fishes darker on their backs than on their under sides? What do fishes eat and how are their teeth suited to their feeding habits? Do fishes see, and hear, and smell, and communicate with each other? How do fishes reproduce and what care do they give their young?

The remaining chapters deal with special groups of fishes. Each includes the classification and identification of the most common members of the group, their distribution, economic importance, and any habits of special interest to the naturalist. The chapters on freshwater and saltwater game fishes describe the common species that make some of our states, from Maine to Florida and from Michigan to California, the mecca of American anglers. Another chapter deals with the food fishes of the sea, such as the herring and cod, that have played an important role in the economy of the New England states. Other chapters take us into the homes of the gaily colored reef fishes of subtropical Florida and into the strange seas that shelter fantastic fishes resembling creatures from another world. We will meet giants and midgets, harmless vegetarians and voracious carnivores, fishes with weapons and venoms and even electric batteries. When you have read the last chapter, you will have a fish-eye view of the variety of species which populate our rivers and ponds and ocean shores.

For the inquiring naturalist, an abundance of excellent books is available on flowers and trees, and on birds and insects. In the realm of fishes, on the contrary, there is no such abundance; in fact the available books are few indeed. It is hoped that *Fishes and Their Ways* will remedy to some extent this lack and will encourage the hitherto land-based naturalist to learn more about life in American waters.

Clarence J. Hylander
Bar Harbor, Maine
February, 1963

Fishes and Their Ways

The sea drum, or black drum, is equipped with the types of fins found in many fishes: a dorsal fin along the back, a tail fin, an anal fin, a pair of ventral fins at the forward end of the body, and a pair of pectoral fins on the side of the head. The "whiskers" are barbels—special sensory structures found on some fishes.

Chapter One

Meet the Fishes

The world in which a fish lives is a far different one from that of a land animal. The aquatic environment shapes the body and influences the habits in such ways that inhabitants of water seem strange creatures to us, accustomed to the demands of living on land. That the underwater world is a fascinating one I am sure we will all agree once we go beneath the surface and mingle with the life of this realm. It is impossible between the covers of a single book to describe all the animals that live in our many rivers and lakes as well as in the sea. We shall therefore limit our attention to those that are undisputed masters of the aquatic world—the fishes.

Before exploring the realm of fishes we should be sure that we know exactly what is meant by a fish. Everything that swims or lives in the water is not a fish even though it may be called so. Jellyfish, for instance, are not fishes but soft-bodied animals known as coelenterates, a group that includes the corals and sea anemones. Starfish likewise are not fishes but members of another group known as echinoderms to which sea urchins and sand dollars also belong. Shellfish are not fishes, either. Some, like crabs, are crustaceans; others are mollusks, such as clams. There also are water-dwellers that look like fishes but are really sea-going mammals—the porpoises and whales.

What Is a Fish?

A fish is, first of all, a vertebrate. This means that *a fish has an internal skeleton of cartilage or bone.* Jellyfish, starfish, and shellfish lack such an internal skeleton and as a result belong to a group of animals known as invertebrates. Possession of an internal skeleton, of which we are reminded when we find bones in the fish on our dinner plates, places a fish in the same category as the other back-boned animals: the amphibians, reptiles, birds, and mammals. All these belong to the vertebrate group of animals, a large and important assemblage in which is man himself. Fishes, however, differ from other swimming vertebrates in a number of ways, most of which are the result of their complete adaptation to living in the water.

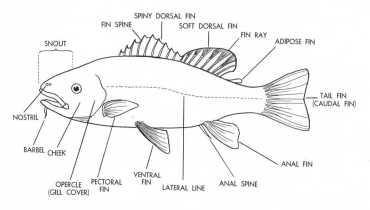

Generalized diagram of features used in fish identification.

A fish has paired appendages in the form of fins. With only a few exceptions, such as lampreys, two sets of paired appendages are typical of fishes, as they are of most vertebrates. The fins of a fish are such paired appendages. A fin lacks the framework of jointed bones that attaches a limb to the body. Fins also lack terminal digits, such as fingers in humans, and the muscles that enable the limb to be used in locomotion.

A fish is equipped with special respiratory organs known as

2

gills by which it can breathe under water. Oxygen is essential for every living organism, and the chief source of oxygen available to a fish is the air dissolved in the water. Water, taken in through the mouth, passes over the gills in the back of the throat. In the gills, dissolved air passes from the water into the blood. An aquatic organism with gills is perfectly adapted for staying under water continuously. On the other hand, an animal with lungs—be it an alligator, a loon, or a whale—must come to the surface periodically to breathe. Gill-breathing is a handicap to living on land; yet some fishes can survive for long periods breathing air if the gills are kept moist.

The body of a fish is covered with scales. Scales are an ideal body covering that provides protection, at the same time permitting the flexibility essential in a swimming animal. Only a few kinds of fishes, notably the moray eel and catfish, lack scales. A similar scaly covering is also a feature of reptiles, which is not unusual when we realize that reptiles are descendants of prehistoric fishes that retained the scales even though they became otherwise specialized for land living.

A fish is a cold-blooded animal, with a body temperature that fluctuates with changes of the temperature in its surroundings. Cold-bloodedness is typical of amphibians and reptiles as well as of fishes. Birds and mammals are the only vertebrates that have developed a means of maintaining a constant body temperature; they are known as warm-blooded animals. This is an important difference between aquatic mammals, such as whales, and fishes.

We therefore can define a fish as a cold-blooded aquatic vertebrate breathing by means of gills, with paired append-ages in the form of fins and with a body covering of scales. This definition applies to the great majority of fishes. Because of these features, fishes are the vertebrates best suited for life in the water, where they are the dominant forms of large animal life. The fossil record tells us that fishes were the first vertebrates to appear in the evolution of life on this planet.

3

This makes fishes a significant group of animals in more ways than one.

The Body Design of a Fish

If a group of engineers should set out to design the ideal underwater, self-propelled mechanism, they could not improve upon the fish. Fishes are living submarines with a body design that combines maximum ease and speed of movement through the water with minimum expenditure of energy. They are without doubt the most perfectly streamlined animals in the world. Unfortunately, most of us see a fish only when it is out of its natural environment—when caught on a hook or thrashing in a net. But even under these conditions a fish is bound to evoke admiration for its streamlined body. The ideal swimming shape is best seen in mackerel and swordfish—the teardrop design. Most game fishes have streamlined designs but to a less perfect degree.

The body design of a typical fish is associated closely with movement through the water; swimming is as much a part of the life of a fish as flying is of birds. The fish is essentially a compact mass of muscle moving through the water. To do this effectively a fish has to have a head and a tail of a certain shape, body proportions of suitable length and cross-section, and body covering and appendages that conform with movement through the water. This ideal shape, or master plan, is like that of a torpedo, pointed or rounded in front, swelling out to the greatest diameter at the shoulders, and tapering gradually to a tail designed to eliminate drag as the fish slips through the water. There are no protuberances, such as external ears, to interrupt the flow of water along the sides of the fish. In the tuna, which rates as one of the fastest swimmers, the fins even fit into grooves when not in use, a design like that of the stabilizers in modern nuclear-powered ships.

This streamlined body is essential for the many kinds of fishes that rely upon speed to catch their prey and escape their

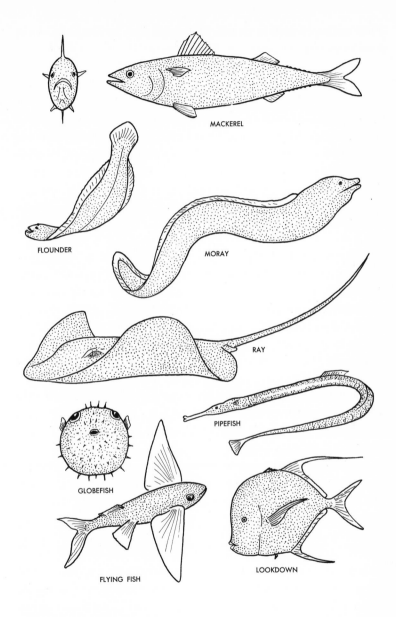

MACKEREL

FLOUNDER

MORAY

RAY

PIPEFISH

GLOBEFISH

FLYING FISH

LOOKDOWN

The body design of fishes reveals a great variety of shapes, each suited to a special way of life.

enemies. Fishes that can get their food and escape capture by predators in other ways often exhibit a different body design. Such can be seen in the cylindrical snakelike body of an eel, the flattened body of a flounder, and the spear-shaped body of a pike. The thin, disklike body of many tropical reef fishes enables them to slip in and hide among the crevices of rocks and corals. One of the many fascinating aspects of fish life is the variety of ways in which their bodies have become adapted to the many different habitats found in the water.

The Body Covering of a Fish

The ideal body covering for a swimming animal is one that at the same time affords adequate protection, permits flexibility of body muscles for swimming, and provides minimum resistance to movement through the water. Scales have all these advantages. The scaly covering is an improved and modernized version of the clumsy armor plate that enveloped the first prehistoric fishes. The separation of armor into small units—the scales—made possible a body as flexible as that of a knight in his coat of mail.

Scales are nonliving structures produced by the skin of a fish. A fish's skin, unlike that of man, is made up entirely of living cells. They can remain alive because the skin, being bathed by water, is rarely exposed to drying out. The fish's skin secretes a slime, or mucus, that produces the slippery surface so typical of most fishes. This acts as a lubricant, enabling the fish to slip through the water. It also protects the body against invasion by bacteria, fungi, and other disease-causing organisms present in water. Protection from external infection is very important to a fish as well as to every other animal. Experienced fishermen and workers at fish hatcheries know that they should wet their hands well before handling a fish that is to be returned to the water. Otherwise much of the protective mucus is removed and the fish is exposed to infection.

Beneath the mucous-covered surface of the skin are the scales, which develop shortly after the fish is hatched. Thus a thin layer of living skin lies over the scales. In some species, such as the freshwater eel, this outer layer is so thick that the small deeply imbedded scales barely are visible. Only in a few fishes are the scales eliminated entirely, as in the catfish family. The forward end of each scale lies in the skin, the posterior lies free and overlaps the following scale much as shingles are arranged on a roof. This permits the water to slip over the scales with little resistance. The visible portion of a scale is much smaller than the part buried in the deeper layers of the skin. This portion of each scale is connected with the underlying muscle tissue; contraction of these muscles results in the oblique position of the scales in the skin.

There are several types of scales. Their nature, size, and number are important aids in identifying different species of fishes. Most primitive is the *placoid scale,* which is the type covering the body of a shark. Each placoid scale resembles a miniature tooth and for this reason is known as a denticle. It is a conical projection with a hard coating of enamel, an inner core of dentine, and a central pulp cavity containing blood vessels and nerves. Similar structures in the jaws of a shark serve as teeth. Placoid scales cause the rough sand-papery texture of a shark's skin, which is known commercially as shagreen. Another primitive type of scale is the *ganoid scale* characteristic of sturgeon. Each ganoid scale is a four-sided plate that fits closely against adjacent plates without overlapping. Such a body covering, being relatively inflexible, is responsible for the stiffness typical of the movements of sturgeons and their relatives.

Most of the fishes commonly found bear *cycloid scales* that are oval or circular in outline and have a smooth exposed margin. Cycloid scales occur among the salmon, trout, and minnow species. The scales may be very small, as in mackerel or herring, or very large, as in tarpon. Cycloid scales make

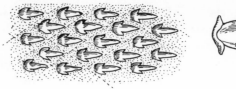
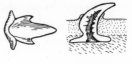

PLACOID SCALES

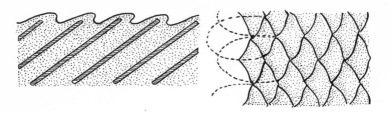

CYCLOID SCALES

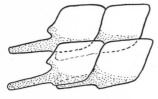

GANOID SCALE

CYCLOID SCALE OF SALMON

CTENOID SCALE OF PERCH

Types of fish scales: placoid scales (dogfish shark), cycloid scales (cod), and ganoid scales (gar). The ctenoid scales of perch and cycloid scales of salmon (bottom) show the annual growth rings.

possible a very supple body, as is shown by the quick movements of a trout darting about its rocky pool. Some fishes have similarly shaped scales but with a margin of comb-like teeth. These are the rough *ctenoid scales* typical of the sunfish family.

The number of scales on the body of a fish remains the same throughout its life. Thus as the fish grows and its body increases in size, the individual scales also must increase in size. Such scale growth is brought about by the addition of new material around the buried edge of the scale, being deposited in rings or layers somewhat as seasonal growth takes place in the wood of trees. In summer a fish, being able to find plenty of food, grows rapidly. During this period the scales also increase in size, the deposition of new material in each scale taking the form of growth rings that are far apart. In winter living conditions are less favorable and the fish grows more slowly. The scales reflect this slower rate of growth, forming rings that are close together and appear as a dark band known as the annual check. The number of annual checks corresponds to the age of the fish. Scales reveal other details of a fish's life also. In salmon they show how many years were spent at sea and how many times the individual has spawned. Even the length of the fish can be estimated from the size of a single scale.

How a Fish Swims

Locomotion in fishes, as in all vertebrate animals, is brought about by contraction of muscles. These muscles are concentrated in the posterior part of a fish, chiefly in the tail region. Only a few muscles are found elsewhere, such as those that open and close the gill covers and move the jaws. The absence of muscles in the face gives a fish its expressionless look. The body muscles are arranged in segments shaped like a **W** lying on its side. Because the muscles make up most of

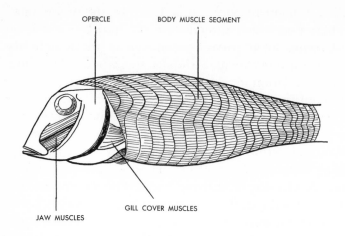

OPERCLE   BODY MUSCLE SEGMENT

GILL COVER MUSCLES

JAW MUSCLES

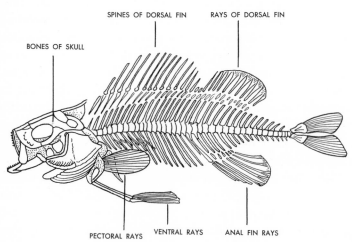

SPINES OF DORSAL FIN   RAYS OF DORSAL FIN

BONES OF SKULL

PECTORAL RAYS   VENTRAL RAYS   ANAL FIN RAYS

The form of a fish's body is determined by the compact mass of muscle tissue and the arrangement of the parts of the skeleton.

the posterior portion of the body, the vital organs—liver, heart, digestive tract—are crowded into a small space behind the head. Muscle tissue, or meat, of a fish is white or grayish in color due to the complete oxidation of food during muscular contraction. The muscle in deep-seated tissues is a darker brown in color; the pink color of salmon muscle is caused by a pigment (lipochrome) derived from the small invertebrates on which salmon feed.

A fish swims by alternate contractions of the muscle segments, first on one side and then on the other. This brings about an undulation of the body, which is transmitted to the main propulsive organ, the tail. Forward movement is the result, just as when a skater moves forward by pushing against the ice with a stroke first of one foot and then of the other. Wavelike undulation of the entire body is typical of slow-swimming fishes with cyclindrical bodies, such as eels; this is the least effective way of utilizing the muscle contractions. Far more efficient is the side-to-side movement of the tail, like the motion of an oar in sculling a boat. Tail propulsion is made even more effective by the shape of the tail fin. A square-cut or rounded tail fin, such as that of cod, is characteristic of a slow swimmer. The slightly forked tail fin of a herring denotes a faster swimmer. A large, deeply forked tail fin of crescent shape, as in the swordfish, is the mark of a very fast swimmer. Such a tail fin functions somewhat like a propeller; the tail and vertebral column act as the shaft, the lobes of the tail fin as the propeller blades.

Scientists have discovered why a forked tail fin is of such an advantage in swimming. The slipstream of water along the sides of a fish converges at the end of the tail. An undivided tail fin creates a drag at this point. But an indentation immediately aft of the tail axis eliminates the portion of the fin that would cause an obstruction to a smooth flow of water past the fish. Champion swimmers, like tuna, have a strong cylindrical tail of small diameter to which is attached a relatively large "propeller." These fishes have been known to keep up with the speed of an ocean liner; in fact they are capable of bursts of speed estimated at 60 miles per hour. Many fishes attain speeds of 30 miles per hour, and salmon can work their way against a river current at the rate of 30 miles per day.

Fins and Their Uses

Fins, although found on practically all fishes, are not indispensable organs. Fins probably arose as a result of the soft, muscular body pushing against the resistant water. Thus a skin-fold or membrane may have been squeezed out at the margins of the body, later to become strengthened by fin rays and spines. It is commonly believed that fishes swim by means of their fins, but as we have just seen, this is a misconception since the main propulsive force comes from the tail. Fins do, however, serve many useful functions. A fish deprived of its fins finds it more difficult to carry out many essential movements. Fins are of two types: unpaired and paired. An *unpaired fin* is a vertical appendage that develops along the midline of the back, the posterior part of the ventral surface, and also terminates the tail. *Paired fins* are located opposite each other on the sides of a fish.

The unpaired fin along the back is the *dorsal fin*. Such a vertical fin (as in an airplane) gives stability to the elongated and often compressed body of a fish, which otherwise might roll from side to side. It also functions as a keel in keeping the fish on a steady course. Its location and appearance are aids in recognizing different groups of fishes. The dorsal fin may be single and low, forming an undulating membrane along the back as in the freshwater eel, or it may be high as in the dolphin. A single dorsal fin characterizes many common fishes. This may be tall and situated far forward as in the swordfish; it may be located midway along the back as in trout; or it may be set far back near the tail as in muskellunge. Some fishes have several dorsal fins: in cod there are three; in barracuda, two. Many fishes have a dorsal fin consisting of two sections, a forward region stiffened with spines and a posterior soft-rayed portion. Fishes with this type of dorsal fin are known as spiny-rayed fishes. The majority of our common game fishes belong to this group.

The *anal fin* is an unpaired fin on the ventral side of the

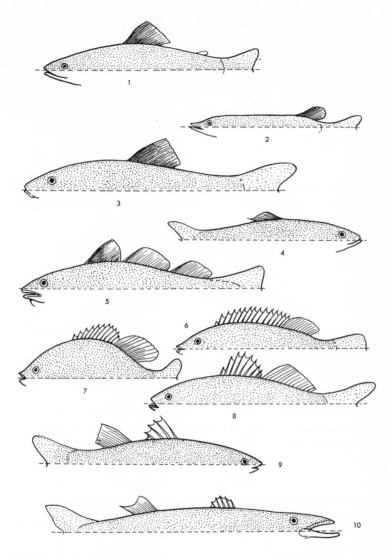

The dorsal fins of fishes are of two main types. Soft-rayed fins occur in the brook trout (1), pickerel (2), sucker (3), herring (4) and cod (5). Stiff spiny-rayed fins occur in the cunner (6), sunfish (7), striped bass (8), mullet (9) and barracuda (10).

fish, between the anus and the tip of the tail. Most fishes have a small and single anal fin, in others it may be larger and more conspicuous. The cod has two anal fins, but in some fishes this fin is lacking entirely. A peculiar type of unpaired fin known as an *adipose fin* can be seen on the back of trout and catfish. This is a fleshy fin of small size located between the dorsal and tail fins. A series of small vertical *finlets* develop on the fishes in the mackerel family, between the dorsal fin and the tail fin, and the anal fin and the tail fin.

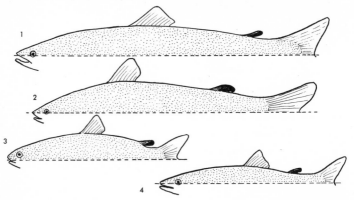

Adipose fins are found in Atlantic salmon (1), catfish (2), whitefish (3) and smelt (4).

Variations in the shape of the *tail fin* also are useful in identifying fishes. In the majority the backbone does not extend into the tail fin, which is symmetrically lobed. In sharks and sturgeons, however, the tail fin consists of two lobes of unequal size, and the backbone extends into the enlarged upper lobe. As has already been mentioned, the shape of the tail fin is correlated with proficiency in swimming.

The paired fins of a fish correspond to the limbs of a land animal. The *pectoral fins* are the two fins that develop, one on either side of the forward end of the fish, near the head. The *ventral fins,* or pelvic fins, are also paired, but they are less constant in their position. In sturgeon and gar the ventral fins are set far back near the tail. In salmon and trout

14

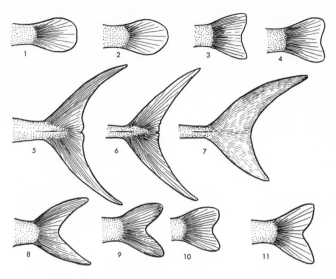

The tail fin may be rounded or square-cut as in sculpin (1), gar (2), brook trout (3), largemouth bass (4); deeply forked as in the swift-swimming swordfish (5), tuna (6), mako shark (7); or moderately forked as in bluefish (8), carp (9), yellow perch (10) and white bass (11).

they are near the middle of the body. In members of the perch and sunfish families they are located far forward near the pectoral fins and below them. In a few fishes, such as those in the codfish family, the ventral fins are actually in front of the pectoral fins. Paired fins are useful in balancing and leisurely swimming; during more rapid swimming the paired fins are folded back against the body. Slow movement of the paired fins enables the fish to remain motionless in spite of the tendency of the stream of water ejected from the gill openings to propel the fish forward. Perhaps the greatest value of the paired fins is their use in maneuvering, making precision movements, and acting as brakes in making quick stops. When the ventral fins are located close to the pectorals, the fish can pivot in a small space; this is of particular advantage to small tropical fishes, which can thus dart in and out of the crevices in rocks. A small number of fishes, because

of a rigid body covering, use the fins for propulsion. The tiny
sea horse swims slowly in a vertical position by whirling its
small dorsal fin like a propeller, and the thick-scaled parrot
fish rows with its pectoral fins.

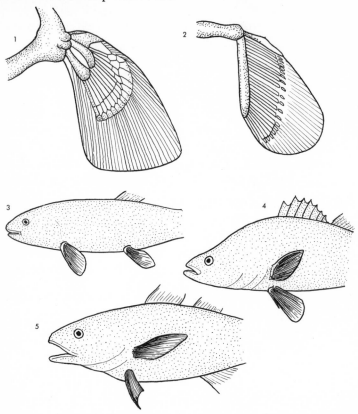

*Upper drawing: the skeletal framework supports the pectoral
fin (1) and ventral fin (2), illustrated in the dogfish. Lower drawings: location of the paired fins varies, as in minnow (3), white
perch (4), and cod (5).*

Fins are versatile organs capable of becoming modified in
many ways. The spines that occur in some types of dorsal
fins are a protection against enemies. Sea robins use their
stiff ventral fins as legs for walking on the ocean bottom.

16

Flying fishes use their expanded pectoral fins as wings when they soar in the air. The ventral fins of male sharks are used as claspers during mating. The strange frogfishes have wrist-like joints at the base of their pectoral fins which enable them to use the fins as if they were hands. These are but a few examples selected at random to illustrate how fins have become modified in many different ways.

The Colors of Fishes

Most fishes of the northern states that are caught for sport or food are attired in modest shades of gray, green, or brown. But in more tropical waters fishes are far more colorful, their hues rivaling those of birds and butterflies. Many of the fishes that live along the Florida and southern California coasts present a dazzling array of colors. Some, like the snapper, are bright red; others, such as the filefish, are golden yellow. Many are deep blue, iridescent green, blue and gold, or jet black. Viewed through the bottom of a glass-hulled boat or at close range when scuba diving, a community of tropical fishes is as colorful a group of animals as one will find anywhere on land.

Scales contribute little to the color of a fish as they are lacking in color-producing substances. They may, however, impart a glassy sheen to the fish by reflecting light rays at different angles. Two substances in the skin, guanin and pigment, are responsible for most of the coloring found among fishes.

Guanin is a waste product which is deposited in the skin as rounded or polygonal plates known as *iridocytes*. When iridocytes are close to the surface they produce the silvery color so prevalent among fishes. When situated deeper in the skin, iridocytes bring about the dead-white color typical of many fishes. Thus the silvery and white colors of fishes are caused by an accumulation of waste products which cannot be disposed of in any other way.

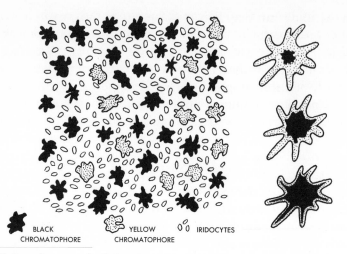

BLACK CHROMATOPHORE   YELLOW CHROMATOPHORE   IRIDOCYTES

Color elements in fish skin. Chromatophores and iridocytes are both found on the upper side of a flounder (left). In some chromatophores (right) the pigment can be condensed in the center of the cell, or spread out to all parts of the cell.

Pigments are produced in special skin cells known as chromatophores. A *chromatophore* is a branching cell with a central body and radiating arms; each chromatophore contains only one kind of pigment, usually red, yellow, or black. Only living chromatophores can manufacture these pigments. Thus many brilliantly colored fishes quickly lose their colors after being caught. A fish that is entirely red has chromatophores with that particular pigment, distributed all over the body. Many fishes, however, have a color pattern resulting from chromatophores with one kind of pigment in one region, chromatophores of another type elsewhere. When they are mixed without any definite pattern, a blended coloring results, such as the mottled or speckled greens and browns of many game fishes. Fishes like sharks, which lack chromatophores, are gray in color.

Light is an important factor in the development of chromatophores. This is one reason that many fishes are more colorful on the back, which receives direct illumination, than

18

on the under surface. It is also the reason that many tropical fishes are so colorful, living as they do in an environment of great light intensity. In a typical fish the ventral surface is silvery white because of the predominance of iridocytes and absence of chromatophores. The lighter hues of the sides result from a mingling of iridocytes with comparatively few chromatophores. The more pronounced colors of the back are caused by an abundance of chromatophores and fewer iridocytes. It is a popular belief that the lighter underparts of a fish and the darker colored back are protective adaptations that make the fish less conspicuous from below as well as above. But this distribution of color can better be explained as a result of a fish's physiology: the accumulation of iridocyte wastes in certain parts of the body, and the development of pigments in other parts.

Brilliant colors are of little value as camouflage. But the more inconspicuous colors and patterns render a fish less noticeable in its natural surroundings. The mottled brown of a skate lying partly buried in the bottom, the muddy colors of a sculpin, the speckled brown of a trout, and the green of a pickerel are undoubtedly of such value. One of the remarkable aspects of protective coloration is the ability of many fishes to change their color and pattern to match that of the surroundings. This is possible because the movement of the pigment in a chromatophore is under control of the nervous system. When the pigment is concentrated in the central body of the chromatophore, a gray or neutral tint results. When the pigment diffuses into the branching processes of the cell, the fish assumes the color of the pigment. Groupers are past masters at this type of color change and for that reason have been called the chameleons of the sea. But most incredible of these quick-change actors are the flounders. A flounder is mottled in white, brown, and black—a color mixture that resembles the sediments on which the fish lies. It has been demonstrated in laboratory experiments that flounders can change the pattern of their light and dark markings to match that of the particular kind of surface on which they are placed. The result is as effective a camouflage as found in any kind of animal. Biologists have discovered that vision plays an important role in this process, for blindfolded flounders lose the ability to carry out this pattern change.

In many species the individual fish develops different colors and patterns depending upon its age and sex, the temperature of the water, the nature of the bottom, and the time of the year. Every fisherman knows that trout vary in color according to the stream in which they are caught, the nature of the lake or stream bed and the time of the year. Salmon are a different color when just returning from the sea than when established in a stream or lake. Male salmon assume a bright red color during the spawning season. For these reasons, the color of a fish is often an unreliable feature in identifying a species. To the naturalist accustomed to using color as an aid in identification (as can often be done with insects, birds, and reptiles), this presents a frustrating obstacle in the study of fishes. As we meet in later chapters representative fishes found in our streams, ponds, and ocean waters, we shall rely for their identification on the more constant features such as body proportions, type and location of fins, size of scales, location of mouth and the type of teeth.

The Size of Fishes

It is human nature to be fascinated by superlatives, especially those dealing with the "largest" and the "smallest" of any kind of plant or animal. Superlatives are interesting to biologists also because unusually huge bodies or unusually small ones reveal the remarkable ability of organisms to use the same blueprint and structure in a fish weighing ounces and one weighing tons. The mature size of an animal is determined by a combination of heredity and environment. Heredity sets the upper and lower limits for a species, within which the actual size will vary as conditions in the environment favor or hinder growth. A common minnow, for example, ranges in size from a few inches to almost a foot. It would be surprising to find one of these minnow species growing to the size of a tuna. The maximum size within the limits of a particular species is determined by suitable temperatures, ample food, and an absence of enemies (including fishermen!). A fish, unlike most animals, can grow throughout its life. Thus the longer it lives the larger it can grow, limited only by the hereditary maximum for the species. It is common knowledge that in accessible fishing areas most of the game fishes caught today are not so large as they averaged several decades ago. But at the same time it is true that the largest fish may not necessarily be the oldest one. The exceptionally large fish may be one that has been able to grow rapidly under the most favorable living conditions.

Fishes exhibit a greater range in size than any other group of vertebrates. A whale, the largest mammal, is only 500 times greater in length than the shrew, the smallest mammal. But the largest fish, a whale shark, is 2000 times the size of the smallest fish, a Philippine goby. The search for the largest and the smallest species of fishes has been well documented by Dr. E. W. Gudger, ichthyologist of the American Museum of Natural History in New York. According to Dr. Gudger, the undisputed giant among fishes is the tropical whale shark, a mammoth fish reaching a length of over 40 feet and a weight of at least 13 tons. Sport fishermen consider that they have hooked a huge fish when they have landed a California sea bass measuring 7 feet and weighing 500 pounds, or a bluefin tuna 14 feet long and weighing 1600 pounds. But the real giants are those whose weight is measured in tons rather than pounds, fishes that obviously cannot be caught by the rod-and-reel angler. Most of these are members of the shark families. The man-eating white shark grows to a length of 21 feet and a bulk of 3 tons. The basking shark, the largest species of northern seas, attains a length of 30 feet and a weight of 4 tons.

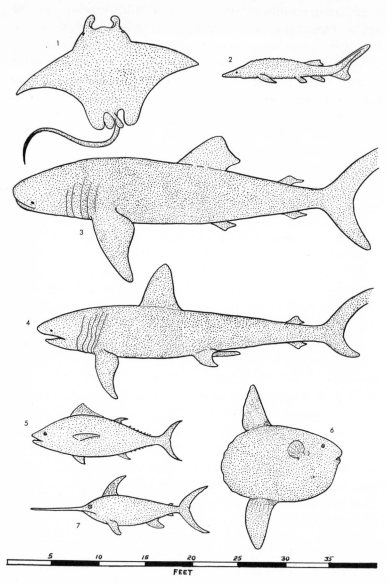

Relative sizes of some giants among the fishes: manta (1), sturgeon (2), whale shark (3), basking shark (4), bluefin tuna (5), ocean sunfish (6), swordfish (7).

Freshwater fishes do not reach such huge proportions. An angler considers he is battling a giant when he hooks a muskellunge 5 feet long and weighing 70 pounds. Even the mighty alligator gar grows to a length of only 9 feet, and a weight of 300 pounds. The largest of all freshwater fishes is the white sturgeon of the Pacific Coast waters. This champion attains a length of 12 feet and a weight of 1300 pounds.

Table 1. Champion Heavyweights Among Fishes
(in round numbers)

Species	Length (in feet)	Weight (in pounds)
White Sturgeon	12	1,300
Black Marlin	14	1,500
Swordfish	15	1,100
Bluefin Tuna	14	1,600
Ocean Sunfish	11	2,000
Manta	20 (width)	3,500
White Shark	21	7,100
Basking Shark	30	8,600
Whale Shark	38	26,000

The only freshwater fish to pass the 1-ton mark was a Russian sturgeon caught in the Volga River; this measured 14 feet and weighed 2250 pounds.

Midgets may be less awe inspiring than giants, but the miniature organism is as fascinating to a biologist as the mammoth one. The tiny fish must have the same complex internal organization of bones, muscle, nerves, glands, and digestive organs as larger fish. As a result it is a marvel of intricately small parts, comparable to the tiny electronic mechanisms in an artificial satellite. The smallest fishes are found among the minnows, blennies, gobies, and killifishes. Blennies are common little fishes of tidal pools and floating masses of seaweed; they range in size from 2 to 4 inches. Our native gobies are chiefly marine fishes, under 4 inches in

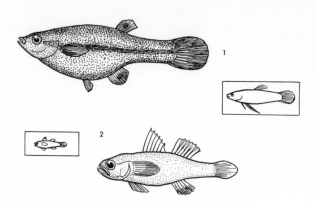

Midgets among the fishes: least killifish (1) and dwarf pygmy goby (2). Actual size is indicated in the rectangles.

length, with the unusual feature of having the ventral fins set so close together they form a sucking disk. For many years the smallest fish was thought to be the least killifish, a member of the live-bearer family found in freshwater habitats of southeastern United States. Its maximum length was 2 inches. But an even smaller fish was found living in a Philippine lake—a tiny goby only one-half inch in length. Even so minute, this goby is an important food fish for the natives. But as it takes 16,000 to weigh a pound, what a tremendous

Table 2. Champion Midgets Among Fishes
(in round numbers)

Species	Length (in inches)
Minnow	3 to 5
Stickleback	2 to 4
Dwarf Herring	2
Dwarf Sea Horse	2
Seaweed Blenny	2
Naked Goby	2
Mosquitofish	2
Least Killifish	1
Pygmy Philippine Goby	2/5

24

number of these gobies must be consumed in a meal for a hungry human! However the present champion, discovered in 1927, is the pygmy goby, also native to the Philippines. It measures only two-fifths of an inch in length. It is not only the smallest fish, but also the smallest known vertebrate.

Where Fishes Live

The distribution of animals is determined by many different factors in their environment. The aquatic environment is far from a uniform one, even though it may seem so from above the surface of the water. Among the varying factors which affect the distribution of fishes are the chemical composition of the water (whether it is fresh, brackish, or salt), its temperature, and the amount of dissolved gases. The last two conditions are associated closely with the depth of the water (water pressure) and its rate of movement.

One of the most obvious differences in the environment of fishes is that of the salinity, or saltiness, of the water. As a result of this, most fishes are adapted for life in either fresh or salt water. Of the approximately 1900 species of American fishes, two-thirds live in the sea, one-third in our streams and lakes. Among the strictly freshwater species are such familiar fishes as minnows, suckers, and sunfishes. Among the common marine fishes are the sharks, mackerels, and flounders. Some families of fishes include species living in fresh water and species living in the sea; this is the case in the salmon, sturgeon, and sculpin families. A small number of species (salmon, trout, eel, shad, and alewife) live part of their life in the sea, part in freshwater habitats.

Some freshwater fishes have established themselves in ice-cold, fast-flowing mountain streams and deep cool lakes, others in warm stagnant ponds and sluggish rivers. Brook trout make their home in cold swift brooks and streams; smallmouth black bass live in equally cool clear lakes. Other slower streams and warmer waters are the home of rainbow trout and white sucker as well as largemouth black bass. Sunfish and perch abound in the smaller warmer ponds with grassy margins, and even somewhat stagnant shallow ponds support great numbers of carp. The oxygen-poor waters of sluggish southern bayous provide a home for the alligator gar, in an environment where many fish cannot survive.

Marine fishes often are classified into three groups on the basis of where they live. Some species are *pelagic,* wandering over the open sea; such are the swift-swimming tuna and swordfish. Other species are *littoral,* staying close to shore in the sheltered waters of inlets and bays or in the surf zone along beaches. Many of these are popular game fishes: striped bass, tarpon, bonefish, and bluefish. Still another group spend their lives on the ocean bottom, grubbing for the mollusks and crustaceans, which are abundant in such places. These are the *benthic* fishes, the bottom dwellers. Some, such as sculpin and flounder, favor the shallow water of bays and harbors. Others, such as cod and halibut, prefer deeper offshore waters. In each of these three groups, the fishes reveal special features that enable them to feed, escape their enemies, and reproduce in their special type of home. If one wishes to identify fishes, it is as important to know where they prefer to live as to recognize their structural features.

At great depths in the sea, miles below the surface, is a realm of eternal cold and darkness, silence, and great pressure. Yet in this seemingly inhospitable environment live many kinds of fishes suited to existing under these unusual conditions. Deep-sea fishes were a lifelong study of the great American naturalist, William Beebe, who documented from firsthand observations the characteristics of these strange animals. His authentic descriptions and photographs bring to light a weird world that exceeds the wildest dreams of a fiction writer. Most deep-sea fishes are of small size, only a few inches in length; all are carnivorous because of a lack of marine vegetation in the lightless depths. Many species have cavernous mouths armed with a murderous array of teeth.

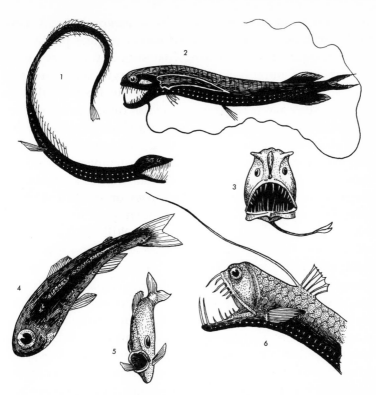

Strange fishes live in the depths of the sea: serpent dragon (1), emerald bow dragon (2), deep-sea angler (3), lantern fish (4), hatchetfish (5) and dragonfish (6). Adapted from E. Bostlemann illustrations in Beebe, "Depths of the Sea," National Geographic Magazine.

Some have huge eyes, and others bear light-producing organs on various parts of their body. Among these deep-sea fishes are distant relatives of such familiar species as herring, eel, and salmon. Others are members of unique families such as the dragonfishes and the lantern fishes. All, however, show the persistence of life in attempting to colonize every available type of habitat.

Another unusual home for fishes is found in the desert. One would not expect to find fishes in Death Valley, yet the hot springs and streams flowing from them teem with killi-fishes, living in water too hot for comfort if one plunges his hand in it. In the hot springs of Nevada other species of killifish have been found in water with a temperature of 204° F. at the surface and 120° F. near the bottom. In such an unusual home these tiny fishes dart about as unconcern-edly as minnows in a New England pond. It is believed that the ancestors of these fishes survived the Ice Age and gradu-ally became adapted to the warming water over a period of many thousands of years. Some of these present-day killifishes actually die if the water temperature drops below 128° F.

The Classification of Fishes

When a biologist studies a large group of animals, such as fishes, he is confronted by a bewildering multitude of thou-sands of different species. He soon notices, however, that certain basic similarities and differences exist that make it possible to separate the species into groups. A particular kind of biologist known as a *taxonomist* specializes in classi-fying these groups into an orderly system. The principle is the same as that employed in setting up a filing system or a collection of postage stamps. Similar things are put together in one category, and then related categories are placed to-gether into a larger unit. Thus the taxonomist arranges sim-ilar species into families, and families with similar features into larger units known as orders and classes. The result is a biological filing system. This makes it easier to find out what a particular kind of fish is as well as to understand the relationships that exist among groups of fishes. Knowing ex-actly what species of fish one is dealing with is essential to the fisherman as well as to the ichthyologist, to the naturalist as well as to the scuba diver.

All fish species are "filed" in three large categories or classes on the basis of their skeleton and type of mouth. (1) All fishes with a skeleton of cartilage, or gristle, and with a

mouth that lacks movable jaws are placed in the class
AGNATHA. Because of their peculiar mouths, they are popularly known as the jawless fishes. (2) The fishes that have a
cartilage-type of skeleton but possess a mouth with movable
jaws are placed in the second class, the CHONDRICHTHYES. In
common parlance, these are known as the cartilaginous fishes.
(3) Fishes with a skeleton of bone—and that includes all the
remaining fishes—make up the third class, the OSTEICHTHYES.
They are known as the bony fishes. Bony fishes possess a
mouth with movable jaws, and thus, in this respect, are like
the preceding class.

The *jawless fishes* are the most primitive of living vertebrates. They are eel-like fishes with a circular suckerlike
mouth. The slimy body lacks a covering of scales, which is
typical of the other two classes of fishes. The gill chamber
opens to the exterior by means of a series of pores, like small
portholes along the side of the head. The most common
representative of this class is the lamprey, a fish of both salt
and fresh waters.

The *cartilaginous fishes,* a larger and more important class,
are more advanced than the jawless fishes in structure and
habits but in other ways are more primitive than the bony
fishes. Cartilaginous fishes have a body covering of placoid
scales; the gill chamber opens to the exterior by a series of
slits on the side of the head or on its under surface; the
mouth in most species has jaws well armed with sharp teeth.
In addition, these fishes possess paired fins. All members of
the class live in salt water only and reveal two trends in body
design. In one group, which includes the sharks, the body is
elongated and streamlined, suited for an active pelagic life.
Sharks, as we have seen, are the largest of all the fishes; they
are also among the most voracious of the predators in the
sea. Sharks have a very ancient lineage that extends backward in time for several hundreds of millions of years. The
other body design, typical of the skates and rays, is that of a
flattened body, triangular or circular when viewed from

above. This associated with the more benthic type of living habits developed by this group of cartilaginous fishes.

The *bony fishes* form the largest and most varied group of living fishes. They make up the most familiar and common of our native fishes—the game fishes, food fishes, and aquarium fishes. Like the cartilaginous fishes, bony fishes have paired fins and mouths usually provided with teeth. They differ, however, in being covered with ganoid, cycloid, or ctenoid scales instead of placoid ones, and in having a single large opening on the side of the head, which leads into the gill chamber, protected by a gill flap or opercle. The detailed classification of the bony fishes is too complex for the layman. It will suffice for our purpose to subdivide the class into three groups with outstanding differences. The most primitive group is that of the sturgeons, featuring ganoid scales and a skeleton that consists mainly of cartilage with some bone. A second group includes the gars and their relatives, also with ganoid scales but with a skeleton made up of more bone and less cartilage. The third group includes all the remaining fishes with a skeleton made up more completely of bone; they are known as the *teleosts*.

Table 3.
Families of Fishes with Soft-Rayed Dorsal Fins

Family	*Habitat*	*Examples*
HERRING	Fresh and Salt Water	Alewife, Shad, Herring, Menhaden
SALMON	Fresh and Salt Water	Salmon, Trout, Whitefish
SMELT	Fresh and Salt Water	Smelt
PIKE	Fresh Water	Pickerel, Pike, Muskellunge
MINNOW	Fresh Water	Minnow, Shiner, Dace, Carp
KILLIFISH	Fresh and Salt Water	Killifish, Topminnow
SUCKER	Fresh Water	Sucker, Redhorse
CODFISH	Chiefly Salt Water	Cod, Haddock, Pollock, Hake
BONEFISH	Salt Water	Bonefish
SHARK	Salt Water	Sharks

Table 4.
Families of Fishes with Spiny Dorsal Fins

Family	Habitat	Examples
BARRACUDA	Salt Water	Barracuda
BILLFISH	Salt Water	Marlin, Sailfish
BLUEFISH	Salt Water	Bluefish
DRUM	Chiefly Salt Water	Drum, Croaker, Kingfish
JACK	Salt Water	Amberjack, Pompano
MACKEREL	Salt Water	Mackerel, Tuna, Albacore, Bonito
MULLET	Fresh and Salt Water	Mullet
PERCH	Fresh Water	Yellow Perch, Walleye, Darter
SCULPIN	Fresh and Salt Water	Sea Raven, Cabezon, Sculpin
SEA BASS	Fresh and Salt Water	White Perch, Sea Bass, Grouper
SNAPPER	Salt Water	Snapper
SUNFISH	Fresh Water	Sunfish, Black Bass, Crappie

Teleosts include a great number of families, each with its unique features. In the flounder family, both eyes are on the same side of a strangely flattened body. In the flying fish family the pectoral fins have become modified into winglike appendages. The catfish family is characterized by whisker-like feelers on the head, and the swordfish family by an upper jaw elongated into a swordlike structure. Many of the teleosts, however, are much alike in their general features but reveal differences in the development of their fins. In one group, known as the *soft-rayed fishes,* the dorsal fin lacks spines. Table 3 indicates some of the families in this group and their representatives in the United States. In another group the dorsal fin is stiffened by spines; hence these are known as the *spiny-rayed fishes.* The spiny-rayed fishes, as can be seen from Table 4 also, comprise a good share of the most familiar fishes.

Many fishes depend upon camouflage for protection. Past master at this art of deception is the sargassum fish, whose fins and outgrowths resemble the sargassum seaweed surrounding it. A second fish, almost invisible, hides at the lower right. Marineland of Florida

Chapter Two

How Fishes Live

As we watch a fish swim without apparent effort in the sunlit clear water or rest among the bright green aquatic plants, we may think that its life is a carefree and easy one. But the life of a fish is a never-ending struggle for existence. All its activities are directed toward either individual survival or perpetuation of its kind. In order to survive as an individual, a fish must be able to obtain food, be aware of changes in its surroundings, and escape the attacks of predators. To survive as a species, fishes must produce adequate numbers of young. How and what fishes eat, how they adjust to their environment, how they protect themselves, and how they reproduce determine the many different ways in which fishes live.

Feeding Habits of Fishes

Fishes, like all animals, must eat to get the energy required for living. Thus the availability of suitable food is a factor of prime importance. *Ecologists*—biologists who study the relations of organisms to their environment—have discovered that all the plants and animals living together in the same area form a closely knit community. The members of this

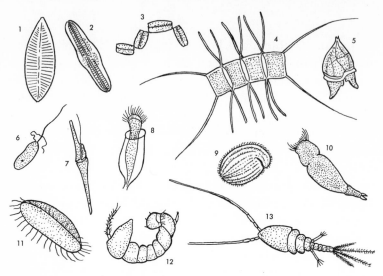

The basic food of all fishes is plankton. Plant plankton includes diatoms (1, 2, 3, 4) and motile flagellates (5, 6, 7). Animal plankton includes protozoa (8, 9), rotifers (10), coelenterates (11), and copepods (12, 13).

community do not feed in a haphazard fashion but according to a definite pattern whereby food (energy) passes from one type of consumer to another. This interrelation of feeding habits results in a *food chain*. Each kind of organism in the community is a link in this chain. When all the links are intact, a self-perpetuating or balanced community is maintained. But if a single link is destroyed, it often has a far-reaching effect on other organisms in the community.

A food chain begins with the organisms that can manufacture their own food. These are the *food-producers*. They are able to synthesize food out of inorganic materials by using the energy of sunlight through photosynthesis, a photochemical reaction uniquely present in green plants. The dominant food-producers in the water are simple leafless plants known as algae. Freshwater algae form the pond scums and greenish coatings on submerged stones and logs. In the sea, algae are the seaweeds that grow along the shore and on the ocean bottom. The most significant food-producers

34

are not the visible algae but the many kinds of microscopic plants drifting about unseen in both fresh and salt water. These unattached plants form part of the *plankton,* a name given to minute floating plants and animals found in streams, lakes, and the sea. Plant members of the plankton are the basic food-producers in aquatic food chains. The most abundant of these are the unicellular, yellowish-brown diatoms. If plant plankton were suddenly to vanish, perhaps destroyed by excessive radioactive wastes dumped into the water, all animal life of that area would come to an end.

All animals are *food-consumers* and are supported by the food-producing plants of the community. There are three types of consumers: herbivores, carnivores, and omnivores. *Herbivores* are the vegetarians, which feed directly on the food-producers; carp and angelfish are among the few herbivorous fishes. *Carnivores* are meat eaters, feeding on the herbivores. They thus are dependent indirectly upon the plants. Some carnivores eat other carnivores as well and as a result are removed still further from the fundamental food source. The great majority of fishes are carnivores; familiar examples are mackerel and trout. The third type of consumer, the *omnivore,* eats any kind of available food, plant or animal; catfish and sucker are omnivorous fishes. The accompanying food-chain diagrams illustrate typical feeding relationships in aquatic communities, indicating the most common herbivores, carnivores, and omnivores. Since fishes often do not confine their feeding to one special category, it is impossible in a simple illustration to show all these possible variations.

The *first consumer level* in a food chain includes the microscopic herbivorous animals that make up the animal plankton. These drifting animals include the single-celled protozoa and the tiny crustaceans known as copepods. This animal plankton is a vital link between the plankton food-producers and all fishes. The floating pastures of ponds and oceans are grazing grounds where billions of minute herbivores transform plant food into animal tissue. Plankton is

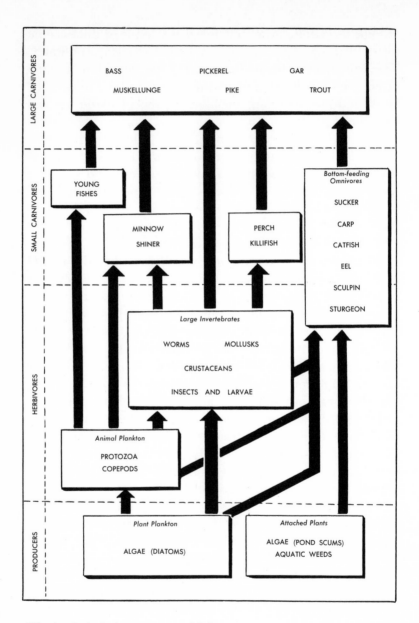

The food chain in streams and lakes.

important in the aquatic food chain in at least three ways. It is the "baby food" for all young fishes and thus of tremendous importance in the growth of fish populations. Some newly hatched fishes subsist on plankton for only a few months; others may do so for several years. Plankton is also the chief diet of the many large invertebrates that abound in the water, such as worms, mollusks, crustaceans, and insect larvae. These in turn are the staple diet of many fishes. A third way in which plankton is important is its direct consumption by small fishes, such as herring. Known as filter-feeders, such fishes have special strainers in the throat by which the minute food particles are filtered out of the water. The strainers, known as gill rakers, are comblike or sievelike structures attached to the gill supports. Surprisingly, some large fishes, such as the basking and whale sharks, are also filter-feeders.

Carnivores and omnivores make up a *second consumer level* in the aquatic community. Among the carnivores at this level are the mackerel and bluefish, which feed in the open sea on such smaller fishes as herring and menhaden. A large number of carnivorous fishes feed on the mollusks and crustaceans that live on the bottom of the sea. Among these benthic species are mullet, cod, and flounder. Fishes living in streams also find much of their food on the bottom; they consume snails, crayfish, and the larvae of aquatic insects. Trout and bass, as the fly fisherman knows, are carnivores that specialize in eating insects and their larvae. The bottom sediments of ponds include, in addition to these invertebrates, a large amount of plant debris—seeds, bits of foliage, and algae. Thus many bottom-feeders in fresh water, such as sturgeon, are omnivorous. The feeding habits often suit the kind of food at hand. Carp is omnivorous when it scoops up bottom debris, herbivorous when it scours algae off rocks, and carnivorous when it feeds on snails and other small invertebrates.

Among the fishes at the *highest consumer level* are the

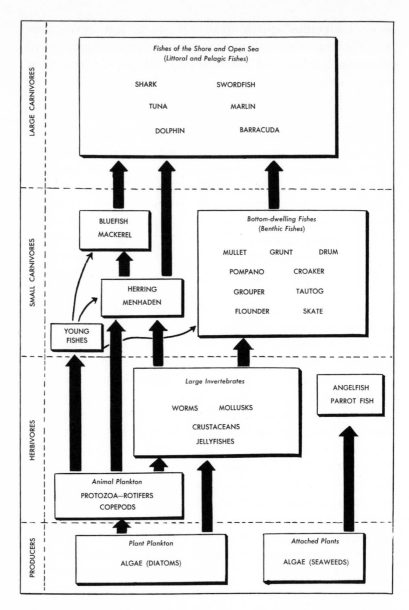

The food chain in the sea.

large carnivorous species that can catch and devour the smaller carnivores. Such are the voracious gars and pikes of freshwater habitats and the sharks and barracudas of the sea. When a fisherman lands a large carnivore such as these, he is collecting the end-product of an intricate food chain that began with the minute copepods and microscopic diatoms. Thus the aquatic community is a complex pattern of pathways by which energy is passed on from one level to another. The food manufactured by the plants of the plankton passes through the microscopic herbivores and smaller omnivores, thence to the larger carnivores and finally to the "top carnivores" such as tuna and swordfish.

The feeding habits of a fish often are revealed by the nature of its mouth and teeth. The *mouth* of a fish may be located on the upper side of the head, at the tip of a pointed snout, or on the under side. A surface-feeding fish, such as the stickleback, which eats mosquito larvae, has the mouth on the upper side of the head. A bottom-feeder has the mouth conveniently located on the under side of the head, as is the case with sturgeon or skate. In some cases the mouth is equipped with fleshy lips, which aid in grasping the food. A long, pointed snout, terminating in a large mouth with powerful jaws, is typical of the predator that relies on quick thrusts to catch its prey. This is true of barracuda and gar. A huge mouth, as found in catfish, is an obvious advantage in engulfing a meal of small fishes or invertebrates. A very small mouth, as in the sea horse, can be used only for feeding on very small aquatic organisms.

The *teeth* of fishes are not used for chewing, as a fish gulps its food whole. The chief function of teeth is to get a firm hold on slippery prey. Fishes differ from land animals in having teeth located in various places in the mouth and throat. In addition to the usual jaw teeth, small *vomerine teeth* develop in the roof of the mouth of some fishes, as in rainbow trout. Lampreys have *rasping teeth* on the tongue. Many fishes in the minnow and sucker families have special

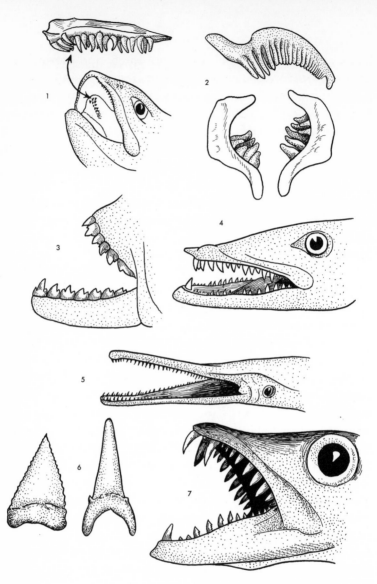

Fishes have teeth in various places in their mouths and throats. Vomerine teeth in the roof of the mouth can be seen in brown trout (1). Pharyngeal teeth in the throat are typical of redhorse and creek chub (2). Jaw teeth are conspicuous in such carnivores as piranha (3), barracuda (4), gar (5), sharks (6), and cutlass fish (7).

pharyngeal teeth in the pharynx, or throat that aid in crushing plant food and other coarse items in the diet. The *jaw teeth* of fishes are not anchored in bone and thus are easily lost, but they are replaced as readily. In sharks, each tooth is like a placoid scale and arises in the fleshy part of the jaws. There may be as many as seven visible rows of sharply pointed teeth. Behind the functional rows are immature teeth that move forward to replace older teeth as they are lost. This constant growth of shark's teeth accounts for their frequent occurrence on ocean beaches. In the bony fishes, teeth are either minute or absent in the herrings, minnows, and suckers. Herbivorous fishes often have teeth that can scrape algae off rocks and coral; in parrot fish the front teeth are fused to form a beak the fish uses in this way. Carnivores that feed on shelled animals have conical or millstone-like crushing teeth, as can be seen in the skates. Knife-like or dagger-like teeth occur in such fierce carnivores as gar, cutlass fish, and piranha.

The voracious feeding habits of large carnivorous fishes make them a potential danger to swimmers. Sharks and barracudas are the most notorious of this type and are often man-killers. Fortunately for visitors to North American beaches, the most dangerous sharks are tropical and so are rarely found off most of our shores. The great barracuda, which has been known to sever an arm or a leg of a man, is also a warm-water fish that is rare along most of our shoreline. A little fish known as the piranha, less than a foot in length, makes up in savagery for its lack of size. This sunfish-like species, which lives in the Amazon River region, has a deceptively harmless appearance, except for the bulldoglike jaws and large, triangular teeth. These teeth are so sharp that South American natives use them as knives and arrowheads. A piranha can shear off a chunk of flesh with one bite of these teeth. Since these killers travel in packs and do not hesitate to attack prey many times their size, a swimmer can lose an arm and a lot of blood in a few moments. There are many stories of the lightning speed with which a pack of piranhas have killed a man. In one authentic case, a drowned boy was reduced to a skeleton in a few hours.

Unique feeding habits occur in the archerfish (2) and angler-fish (1).

Fishes have developed many unique feeding habits. The tiny pipefishes and sea horses suck in minute organisms through their tubular snouts. The blood-sucking lamprey can attach itself to another fish, rasp a hole in the skin, and feed on the blood of the luckless victim. The anglerfish is equipped with a simulated rod and bait, used to lure small fishes into its cavernous mouth. But perhaps the most unique is the method by which the archerfish of southeastern Asia can "shoot" insects off an overhanging leaf and knock them into the water. This sharpshooter among fishes has excellent vision even when the insects are on land and five or six feet distant. By ejecting a pellet of water with a remarkably accurate aim, the fish hunts for its meals out of the water. The "gun" consists of a lengthwise groove in the roof of the mouth; when the tongue presses against this groove, a tube is formed through which a droplet of water can be ejected at high speed.

How Fishes Adjust to Their Surroundings

The environment of a fish presents many different stimuli to which the fish responds in order to obtain food, avoid extremes of temperature and pressure, find its way to a spawning ground, or to escape enemies. Some of these are like the stimuli governing the reactions of land animals; others are peculiar to the environment in which a fish lives. Response to these stimuli depends upon the presence of sense organs. Most fishes rely upon vision for getting food, escaping predators, and recognizing other fishes. Thus the eye is a vital sense organ. Fishes rely also on their sense of smell to locate food; thus olfactory organs are important to fishes. Other senses are those of touch, taste, hearing, equilibrium, and pressure detection.

Vision, as in all higher vertebrates, is the function of the eyes. A fish's eye is fundamentally like our own. It consists of a spherical eyeball with a transparent covering (cornea) as an outer protection in front of the iris and with a lens for focusing the light rays on the retina. There are, however, some significant differences. The eyeball has no eyelids and there are no tear glands, both unnecessary under water. A few fishes have special types of eyelids, but none has the opaque lids typical of mammals. The pupil of the iris is an opening of fixed diameter, but this is no handicap because illumination under water is never so brilliant as to require an adjustable diaphragm. The lens is spherical and of a fixed curvature instead of flattened and capable of change as in the human eye; thus the eye of a fish is like a fixed-focus camera. The focus in bony fishes is set for a distance of a few feet; such nearsightedness does not put the fish at a disadvantage since water is usually too turbid for vision at great distances. In addition, these fishes are ordinarily interested

43

only in objects near at hand. The lens is set for more distant vision in sharks, as might be expected from the feeding habits of these carnivorous fishes.

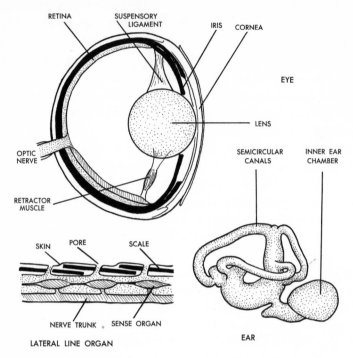

Sense organs of a fish.

The eyes of a fish are located on either side of the head, each thus producing a separate image. This lack of stereoscopic vision, such as humans possess, does not eliminate the ability of some fishes to judge distances. Fish vision includes also a vague discrimination between light and dark objects and in some species even between colors, provided the object is under water. Sport fishermen are sure that game fishes do perceive colors, as the great variety of artificial flies seems to prove. Many fishes, of which cod is an example, can move their eyes only very little; this gives such fishes the fixed stare associated with a "fishy eye." Fishes that live at depths of 300

44

to 1500 feet often have extremely large eyes as do those with nocturnal feeding habits, like the tropical squirrelfish. Fishes living at great depths where light does not penetrate have small or imperfect eyes or none at all. Over sixteen families of fishes include species that are totally blind. These blind fishes live in caves or other subterranean habitats where it would be difficult to see even with excellent eyes. It is believed that many such blind fishes originally had small undeveloped eyes—a condition occurring in many species of lighter habitats—but lost their vision completely after migrating into the lightless environment.

Hearing in fishes depends upon two types of sense organ. Sounds of low frequencies, in the range of 50 to 300 vibrations per second, are sensed by the *lateral line organ,* a unique structure found in fishes. The lateral line forms a stripe along the side of a fish from gill opening to tail. It is present in most fishes, notable exceptions being the herring and salmon families. The lateral line is a mucous-filled tube that opens to the surface by a series of pores. Beneath this tube lies a long nerve that sends out branch nerves into the canal, each branch ending in a small sense organ. These are sensitive to low-frequency vibrations and can detect the passing of another fish or the nearness of an obstacle by vibrations reflected from it. The lateral line organ may also be a temperature detector warning the fish when it enters water that is too warm or too cold; this is important because fishes are extremely sensitive to rapid temperature changes. The lateral line was formerly thought to be concerned with the detection of currents and thus with guiding migrating fishes, but this function is not definitely proved.

Fishes have no external ears but possess *inner ears* located behind the eyes and near the brain. Each ear is a series of canals or chambers buried in the bones of the skull. Sounds of higher frequencies are perceived by this inner ear. Although a fish cannot detect so wide a range of sound vibrations as humans can, a special chamber in the inner ear registers up to 2752 vibrations per second. When this part of the ear is destroyed, the fish can hear only the low frequencies sensed by the lateral line organ. The inner ear also includes the *semicircular canals* that, as in higher animals, are sensitive to changes in position and thus function in maintaining equilibrium.

The sense of *smell,* or the olfactory sense, is highly developed in many fishes. A pair of nostrils is situated in front of each eye, leading into a blind sac where the olfactory cells are located. The nostrils are not a passageway to the throat as in mammals. Chemical substances diffused in the water stimulate these olfactory cells. These substances, given off by dissolving food particles and blood, are sensed quickly, often at great distances. Sharks depend on their unusually keen sense of smell, in contrast to the bony fishes, which rely more upon sight. *Taste* organs, present on the tongue, enable a fish to detect the difference between sour, salt, and bitter substances. *Touch* is a generalized sense made possible by many simple nerve buds scattered over the entire body. The senses of smell, taste, and touch are combined in the feelers (barbels) of such fishes as sturgeon and catfish, which make use of these structures in detecting food.

Many fishes possess an unusual internal organ known as an *air bladder* that lies between the stomach and the backbone and is filled with a mixture of gases. Sharks and rays have no air bladders; bony fishes have either a functional one or traces of one. The air bladder may be connected with the gullet, or throat passage, by a tube, as it is in the herring and salmon families. In other fishes it may be sealed off from the rest of the body. Its exact function is not known, but it does play a role in determining the buoyancy of a fish. Fishes are constantly exposed to the pressure of the surrounding water. This pressure tends to make them sink because living tissues are denser than water. To offset this, some fishes secrete large amounts of oil that, being lighter than water, adds buoyancy to their bodies. Another method involves the air

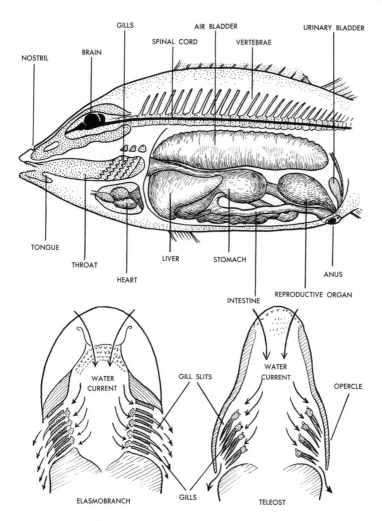

NOSTRIL
BRAIN
GILLS
SPINAL CORD
AIR BLADDER
VERTEBRAE
URINARY BLADDER

TONGUE
THROAT
HEART
LIVER
STOMACH
INTESTINE
REPRODUCTIVE ORGAN
ANUS

WATER CURRENT
GILL SLITS
WATER CURRENT
OPERCLE

ELASMOBRANCH
GILLS
TELEOST

Upper drawing: internal anatomy of a fish. Lower drawing: comparison of gill arrangement in elasmobranchs (sharks) and teleosts (perch).

bladder, which can increase or decrease in volume by absorbing gases from the blood or returning gases to the blood. Thus an air bladder can function much as the ballast tank of a submarine; when the tanks are filled with air, the submarine rises to higher levels; when water is pumped into the tanks, the submarine sinks to lower levels.

Because of an ability to regulate the volume of the air bladder, some fishes can live alternately in fresh and salt water, making possible the migration of fishes from one environment to another. A fish suitably balanced for buoyancy in fresh water is too light when entering the sea and would have to remain near the surface if it had no air bladder to lessen its weight-volume ratio. On the other hand, a fish with an internal buoyancy suited for living in the more dense salt water would tend to sink to the bottom when entering the less dense fresh water of a pond. A fish that cannot change the level at which it finds the most appropriate living conditions in this way, has to do so by a constant expenditure of energy in swimming. The air bladder is also thought to be a pressure gauge that informs the fish when it is descending or ascending too rapidly or entering water of unaccustomed pressure. When a fish descends into deep water the pressure increases, the air bladder is squeezed into a smaller volume. Conversely, when a fish rises to the surface and the pressure suddenly decreases, the air bladder expands and may press against the other internal organs. In either case, the fish is made aware of the pressure change in its environment.

The air bladder has other functions among certain groups of fishes. In some it is a source of auxiliary oxygen supply, and so serves as a respiratory organ enabling these fishes to live for some time in the air. It is also associated with hearing. In cod the forward lobes of the air bladder rest on the inner ears and can conduct sound vibrations to the ear canals. In carp a series of small bones links the air bladder membrane to the inner ear. Thus the air bladder becomes an auxiliary hearing aid, its taut walls receiving vibrations from the rest of the body and passing them on to the ears.

Closely associated with hearing is the ability to make sounds. In recent years much research has been done that

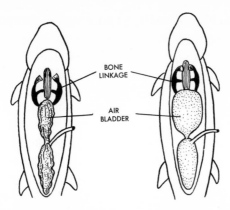

BONE
LINKAGE

AIR
BLADDER

In the carp the air bladder is an auxiliary hearing aid, being linked to the ear by bony levers. When the air bladder is contracted (left) these bones are not in contact with the ear; when the air bladder is distended, the bones fit close to the ear (right).

reveals that fishes, by producing sounds, can communicate with each other, frighten away enemies, and express their feelings. These sounds include a wide range of grunts, groans, croaks, and hums. Many of these sounds are produced in conjunction with the air bladder. Catfish, for example, can make a barking or grunting noise by suddenly expelling air from the air bladder through the duct leading into the throat. An elaborate mechanism found in some South American catfishes makes them very noisy because the sounds are magnified by partitions inside the air bladder. Croakers have special muscles attached to the air bladder that can produce staccato noises like submerged pneumatic drills. Sounds are also produced by other parts of the body. Sculpins can vibrate their gill covers, and the grunts are so named because they can make a grating noise by grinding their pharyngeal teeth together.

How Fishes Protect Themselves

The great majority of fishes are carnivores, preying on other smaller fishes. A fish is constantly exposed to the sudden

49

death of being eaten. Pelagic fishes capable of swimming swiftly rely upon speed for escape. The benthic fishes, on the other hand, have resorted to other ways than speed to escape capture. Some of these methods are passive, such as protective coloration and armor. Others are more aggressive such as the use of weapons, poisons, and even electric shocks to ward off hungry predators.

A fish that can escape notice generally avoids becoming a meal for a larger fish. The effectiveness of *camouflage* in color and pattern already has been described (see page 19). This disguise is very prevalent among bottom-dwelling species and those that live amid aquatic vegetation. A pickerel is practically invisible when poised among the water weeds, as is a mottled flounder on the sea bottom. Camouflage is often enhanced by outgrowths of appendages which give the motionless fish the appearance of being part of the surrounding seaweeds. Fishes of the Sargasso Sea, for example, exhibit an incredible mimicry of their plant neighbors. Such mimicry is also found among many small tropical fishes which live around coral reefs.

A fish that is soft and digestible makes a desirable tidbit for a hungry mackerel or other carnivore, while a fish with a hard, indigestible exterior is usually left unmolested. This must have been equally true of the prehistoric fishes since *body armor* was one of the first protective devices developed by fishes. Such armor, however, is clumsy and heavy and has the added disadvantage of interfering with the flexibility needed for fish locomotion. Today the most completely armored fish is the sturgeon, whose body is covered with bony plates. Most modern fishes have eliminated body armor and come to rely upon other methods of defense. A few fishes have retained the less clumsy armor made of small, tightly fitting hexagonal plates that form a shell encasing the entire fish. This is the case with the tropical trunkfishes. Such fishes, in return for this protection, become practically immobilized in their armor, being able to move only their eyes, lips, and fins.

Spines are a more widespread defensive adaptation in fishes. Spines originated as a support for the otherwise frail fins. But in many fishes the spines have increased in size so that they project beyond the fins or even take the place of parts of the fin, as in the stickleback. Carnivorous fishes undoubtedly prefer a meal that is not spiny and will not stick in their throat. Thus spines are as effective against capture by a hungry fish as they are annoying to a fisherman trying to hold on to a fish he has just hooked. Some fishes have spines elsewhere on the body, also. The inflatable body of a porcupine fish is covered with spines that make the fish as palatable as a pincushion. Sculpins and related fishes have spines on their gill covers that serve the same purpose.

Some types of spines can be used as *weapons* in keeping a predator at bay. The triggerfish, for example, has a stout dorsal spine behind the head that can be locked in place after being erected, making it impossible for a carnivorous pursuer to take the triggerfish into its mouth. The common stingray has a long sharp spine on the top of its whiplike tail. The stingray spends most of the time lying buried in the sand, but if a bather happens to step on the body, the tail automatically arches upward and the spine penetrates his leg. The tropical doctorfish is the most effectively armed of all the weapon-carrying fishes. On either side of the tail is a stiletto-like spine carried in a sheath when not in use. When in danger, the doctorfish can unsheath its dagger, which stands out at right angles to the body; it can be used with dangerous effect as the doctorfish sideswipes an adversary with its tail. The blade of a swordfish can also be used as a powerful weapon. Although usually employed in slashing at schools of small fishes upon which it feeds, a swordfish has been known to attack and pierce a fishing boat with its sword.

Many kinds of animals, from tarantulas to rattlesnakes, capitalize on the effectiveness of *venoms* in warding off the attacks of carnivores. Fishes also produce venoms, although few of our native species do so to a dangerous degree. The madtoms, relatives of the bullheads, possess spines on the pectoral fins that conduct venom from glands at the base of the spines into a careless handler. The effect on a man is only like that of a mild hornet sting, but it would undoubtedly discourage another fish from making a meal of the madtom. Venomous fishes occur in greatest numbers in tropical waters, especially in the Pacific Ocean. An ugly-looking toadfish bears spines on its head that, when pressure is applied to them, can shoot venom a foot or more from its body; the venom easily paralyzes enemies as well as smaller fishes upon which the toadfish feeds. The more beautiful tigerfish, a relative of the American scorpionfish, has an array of long spines on the head and fins that transmit venom to the attacker with painful results.

Spines and poisons make up quite an arsenal of weapons, but fishes are unique in possessing still another means of defense: the ability to deliver an *electric shock*. Fishes are the only animals that are known to generate electricity. Research workers dealing with these unusual fishes say that touching such an electric fish is as unpleasant a surprise as handling an uninsulated wire. Fishes generate the electricity in special organs that are modified muscle, nerve, or glandular tissue. Just how they do it is still much of a mystery. Electric fishes are actually living dynamos capable of producing enough voltage to stun an animal as large as a mule.

In some species the shocking power is relatively mild. The bottom-dwelling stargazer has an electric organ on the head behind the eyes that is thought to be a modified optic nerve. In other fishes the electric organs can generate much greater voltage. In the torpedo, or electric ray, the electric organs are glands located behind the head on each side that can deliver a 220-volt discharge at intervals of a thousandth of a second!

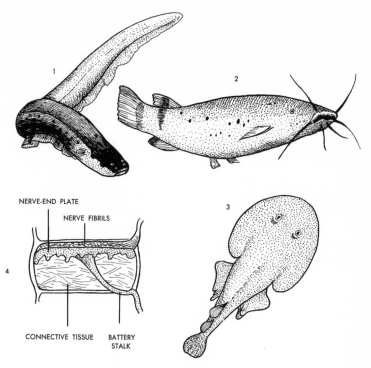

NERVE-END PLATE

NERVE FIBRILS

4

CONNECTIVE TISSUE   BATTERY
STALK

Electricity is generated by special organs in the electric eel (1), electric catfish (2), and electric ray (3). In the ray, the electric battery (4) is a converted muscle cell.

The torpedo uses this power both for defense and for stunning its prey. Another electric species is a catfish of the Nile River region that has glandular batteries all over the body that are also capable of generating about 200 volts. But the electric eel of South America is the most "shocking" of these strange fishes. It is a sluggish eel, 4 to 8 feet in length, living in swamp waters. The electric organ originates back of the head and extends to the tail. Measured by electrical instruments in careful laboratory experiments, the voltage produced by this eel registered 550 volts, with 1000 watts generated. The shock is momentary rather than sustained and cannot be used for such practical purposes as powering electric light bulbs. The strength of such a shock must have a restraining effect on even large predators.

The Family Life of Fishes

The life cycle of a fish begins with the formation of the eggs, or roe, by the female and the production of sperm, or milt, by the male. The essential first step in the birth of a fish is the fertilization of the eggs by the sperm. In most fishes the female releases the eggs into the water, a process known as *spawning*. Spawning ordinarily takes place only once a year. The eggs are fertilized when a male releases milt in the same area. Fishes with this egg-laying habit are said to be *oviparous*. In a few fishes the eggs are retained within the body of the female where they are fertilized and where the young develop. Fishes that give birth to living young in this way are said to be *viviparous*. The family life of fishes differs greatly depending upon whether they are oviparous or viviparous.

Oviparous species display a great variety of spawning habits; they differ in how and where the eggs are laid, how the eggs are protected while hatching, and what care—if any—is given to the young fishes by the parents. Some fishes simply scatter the eggs in the water, trusting to chance that they will be fertilized; other fishes select a breeding site with great care and even make crude nests for the young. A few fishes continue their parental solicitude by guarding the young until they can take care of themselves. In a few cases the fathers even incubate their young in a pouch of their body. It is well known that fishes even undertake long migrations in order to get to a suitable spawning area. This is the habit of salmon and freshwater eels.

The *eggs* of fishes are uniformly small; those of freshwater species are usually a third to an eighth of an inch in diameter, those of marine fishes being even smaller. A smelt's egg is no bigger than the head of a pin, and a herring's egg is only one-twentieth of an inch in diameter. The sea catfish lays the largest eggs, about an inch in diameter. Fish eggs have no shells as do those of reptiles and birds. Instead, each egg is enveloped by a capsule of gelatinous, or jelly-like, material. An exception is the egg of the skate, which is enclosed in a large rectangular black capsule with spiny corners, known commonly as a "mermaid's purse." The number of eggs produced by a single female varies with the size of the fish and the degree of care given to the young. Pelagic fishes that pay no attention to their offspring lay eggs in tremendous quantities. A mackerel lays 500,000 eggs, a striped bass 2,000,000, a sturgeon 2,000,000, a haddock 2,000,000, and a cod 9,000,000. Most of these eggs are eaten by other fishes, but as such great numbers are produced at each spawning, sufficient numbers survive to perpetuate the species. Freshwater fishes that give greater care to their young lay fewer eggs. Black bass lays 20,000 eggs, salmon 8,000, and trout about 1,000.

The eggs, after being fertilized, either float near the surface or sink to the bottom. Cod and mackerel eggs are bouyant and hatch as they float in the water. Most freshwater fishes, and many marine ones, have eggs that are heavy and adhesive and so become attached to stones and seaweeds on the bottom. The eggs of freshwater fishes are often entangled in ribbons or masses of jelly that stick to water weeds; this is true of yellow perch and pickerel. The length of the *hatching period* also varies considerably with different species. It is 4 or 5 months for trout, 1 to 3 weeks for muskellunge, 5 days for mackerel, and only 2 days for menhaden. Development of the eggs is retarded by low temperatures, speeded up by high temperatures. Brook trout eggs, for example, require 44 days to hatch in water at 50° F.; 100 days when the water temperature drops to 40° F.; and 145 days in water as cold as 35° F. When emerging from the eggs, the young fish (known as fry) are only a fraction of an inch in length. They immediately begin foraging on plankton, which, as we have seen in the food chain, makes up the bulk of their diet.

Much research has been carried on in an attempt to discover where fishes spawn, how the young feed, and how they find their spawning grounds. Such knowledge of the spawning habits of fishes is vital to the fisheries of the world. Yet very little is known of the spawning details of many common fishes. There is only fragmentary knowledge, for example, of the life histories of such common game fishes as tarpon, tuna, and swordfish. We do know that most marine fishes rely solely upon producing vast numbers of eggs to ensure the survival of some to maturity. Among the schooling fishes, release of eggs and sperm by many individuals at the same time guarantees that some eggs will become fertilized. But no mating takes place for this purpose and there is no careful selection of a spawning site. Similar casual reproductive habits are found in some freshwater fishes such as carp and sucker. But other freshwater species have developed methods that make more certain the fertilization of the eggs and the survival of the young. Pairing of the male and female, construction of an appropriate "nest" for laying the eggs, care of the eggs while they are hatching and care of the young after they hatch, result in a high level of family life that ensures the survival of the species.

The most dramatic and incredible of all spawning habits is that of the *grunion,* a Pacific Coast smelt. This is a small silvery fish that insists on producing a family the hard way— by mating and laying the eggs on land! Spawning coincides with the maximum high tides that occur twice each month, at the phases of the new and the full moon. The entire life cycle of this fish is arranged so that mating, egg laying, and development of the young is coordinated with the tides and the moon. Thus every two weeks from March to July, grunion congregate by the millions in the surf along certain beaches of southern California. The goal of the spawning grunion is the narrow bit of sand reached by the waves of the maximum high tide. A few minutes after high tide, as if at a prearranged signal, the flashing hordes tumble ashore, borne high on the beach by the crest of a wave. As soon as the grunions are left by the receding wave, each female digs a hole in the wet sand with her tail and, lying half buried, deposits her quota of eggs, which are promptly fertilized by nearby squirming males. All this takes place in less than a minute. As the next wave breaks, the grunions are swept back into the sea. On succeeding days the high tides do not come as far up the beach, and the eggs lie buried and undisturbed in the wet cool sand. The young are ready to hatch when the next of the maximum high tides occur and the waves uncover the grunion nursery. The fry are released and washed from the beach back into the sea. It is thus that the grunions survive as a species, by an instinctive timing which regulates all stages in the process from fertilization to birth of the young.

Typical of the parental care given by some fishes during spawning is that of the *Atlantic salmon*. This fish leaves the sea in spring to enter the streams of Maine and adjacent Canada, selecting those with clear, cool, and deep pools where it can remain in safety for the summer months. In October and November, spawning begins. The female salmon selects a site in a fast-flowing but shallow portion of the stream with a gravelly bottom. There she excavates an egg-pit by turning on her side and flapping her tail vigorously, creating water currents that sweep out a hollow "nest." While she is busy at this task a male hovers nearby to drive off smaller or less aggressive males. When the egg-pit is finished, it measures three feet or more in length and several feet in width. The male and female settle into this hollow, and the eggs and milt are released. When spawning is completed, the female often moves a short distance upstream and excavates another pit, the displaced gravel moving downstream and covering the eggs laid in the first pit. Most of the adults die after spawning, but a small number return to the sea. In the meantime the thick-walled eggs develop slowly and do not hatch until March or April. The fry remain in the gravel for a month or two, then wriggle upward and swim about. The young salmon, known as parrs, have dark stripes on their sides. Parrs remain in the stream for two or three years, during which time they grow to a length of seven inches. Then the time comes to leave fresh water; the parrs turn silvery and migrate to the sea. There they remain for several years, eventually returning to the same streams where they were born to repeat the life cycle.

The spawning behavior of *rainbow trout* is somewhat similar. The female selects a site with a gravelly bottom, often so shallow that her dorsal fin is exposed as she excavates an egg-pit several inches in depth and the length of her body. When the pit is completed, the female and male release the eggs and milt into the "nest." The female covers the fertilized eggs with gravel while the male stands guard to keep away hungry predators. The process is repeated, perhaps every day for a week, until the female has laid all the eggs she will produce that season. In the northern states, rainbow trout spawn from February to June. If the water temperature remains around 50° F. the young hatch in about 30 days. The fry emerge from their hiding places amid the gravel in mid-July. At the end of the first summer the young trout, or fingerlings, are 3 or 4 inches in length and usually reach the legal fishing length the second summer.

Some variations on this pattern occur in the sunfish family. *Smallmouth black bass* is more or less typical of the family's spawning habits. The site selected is usually a gravelly bottom in shallow water near the shore, but it is the male instead of the female that digs the nest. The male clears a circular area whose diameter is twice the length of his body. After the "nest" is completed, the female lays her eggs in the prepared site. Bass eggs are adhesive and become attached to the gravel. The female departs after spawning, but the male remains to guard the eggs; at the same time he keeps them clean and aerated by vibrating his fins over them. The eggs hatch in three or four days; after another few days the dark-colored fry emerge from the gravel. The "nests" of large-mouth black bass are less elaborate and are found at depths of one to three feet over more muddy bottom, often at the base of a submerged stump. Spawning takes place in spring or early summer, varying with the geographic location. In the pumpkinseed sunfishes, the male also constructs the nest and remains to guard the developing young. Pumpkinseeds spawn all through the summer.

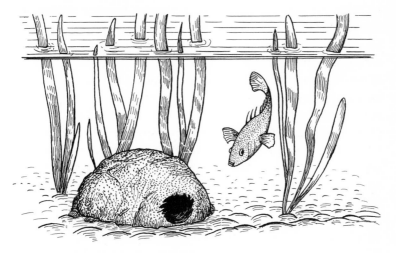

The brook stickleback builds an underwater nest in which the eggs are laid and develop.

The most elaborate nests constructed by any of our native fishes are those of the *brook stickleback,* a small fish only a few inches in length. The male selects a site in a rocky pool where the water flows cool and clear. He then collects bits of vegetation and plant debris, cementing them together by a mucus to form a spherical or barrel-shaped nest. The interior of the nest is tubular, with a front and a back entrance. Often it is weighed down by pebbles and well-concealed amid the water weeds. When the nest is completed, the male escorts a female into it and there she deposits about one hundred eggs. After spawning, the female is driven away by the male who then stands guard until the eggs hatch, a period of about a week. Such extreme parental care assures a large number of young even though relatively few eggs are laid.

An unusual type of parental care exists among some of our marine fishes. In the *sea catfish,* the male picks up the eggs after they are laid and fertilized and stuffs them into his mouth. As many as fifty of the marble-sized eggs are packed away between the floor of the mouth and the gill chambers. For two months the eggs remain there, hatching as they are carried about in safety by the father. This responsibility is inconvenient, to say the least, for the male has to go without eating all this time. At the end of the incubation period, the male becomes a pathetic sight with flabby chin and an emaciated body. But no matter how hungry he is, he does not eat any of the young.

Incubation by the male also occurs in the *pipefish family,* where the young develop in kangaroo-like pouches; the amazing aspect of this habit is that it is the male, not the female, which has the pouch. The mature male pipefish develops two flaps of skin on his abdomen that fuse along their margins to form a pouch open at the upper end. The female, by means of a special egg-laying tube, inserts the eggs into the pouch. The male then fertilizes them and stores the eggs in compact rows until they hatch. During this time the young actually are connected with the body of the male, thereby obtaining their oxygen supply from the father's blood. In a few weeks the eggs hatch and the pouch becomes a mass of tiny squirming pipefish. Then the pouch ruptures along the seam made by the edges of the flaps, and the young are "born alive." Sea horses, also members of this family, follow a similar procedure, except that the pouch does not rupture. Instead, the male has to expel the young one at a time out of the pouch opening, a feat that is accomplished by violent convulsions of the sea horse's body.

The small group of *viviparous fishes* has eliminated the problem of finding suitable spawning grounds, nest-building, and protection of the young. Fertilization of the eggs is guaranteed by the development of structures on the male that make possible direct transfer of the milt into the body of the female. The eggs, internally fertilized in this way, remain within the mother's body where they are safe while hatching. When released, they are free-swimming young fishes capable of taking care of themselves. Sharks and rays have developed this viviparous type of reproduction. The ventral fins of the male shark are modified so that the inner edges have become rodlike claspers used in mating. At birth the young are fairly large, able to swim and feed by themselves. Surfperches are another group of marine fishes that give birth to living young. But best known of the viviparous fishes is the freshwater livebearer family, which includes the mosquitofish. The tropical guppy, also in this family, is a favorite aquarium fish because of its habit of giving birth to living young. The females can be recognized by the swollen abdominal region, where the young develop; the males, by the distinctive anal fins that are specialized for transferring milt to the female. One of the smallest fishes known to man, the least killifish, is also a livebearer.

Migration of Fishes

The term migration is sometimes used in a general sense to describe any wandering of an animal over a considerable distance. In this sense many pelagic fishes are migratory, constantly changing their home as they follow the schools of smaller fishes on which they depend for food. Migration in its strictest biological sense is something different. It is a wandering but to a definite destination for a specific reason. Fishes that migrate leave adequate feeding grounds where they may have been thriving for years to undertake what often becomes a long and dangerous journey simply in order to reproduce.

All fishes do not migrate in this sense; cod and herring, for example, have no such urge. But a great number of other fishes do exhibit a migration pattern as part of their life cycle. Some fishes that live in the sea, such as salmon and shad, migrate into fresh waters to spawn. Other fishes that live in streams and ponds, such as eels, reverse the procedure and go to sea to spawn. Migration is usually a two-way trip, the fishes returning after spawning to the area that their strange urge forced them to leave.

Fish migration is not seasonal as is migration among birds, for winter is no problem to a fish. But fish migration is like that of birds in two respects: it is associated with the reproductive urge, and it involves an uncanny ability to navigate great distances to reach a breeding area. Why and how migration takes place is not yet well understood. Much is still to be learned of the spawning habits of fishes and the migrations associated with spawning. One theory as to why fishes migrate is based on the fact that an internal pressure may build up within the fish, acting as a stimulus to migration. Such an increase in blood pressure may be related to the production of sex hormones by the maturing sex organs. Eels, for example, develop a great increase in internal pressure just before they leave the rivers to enter the sea. If restrained, they become restless and uncomfortable; their bodies swell and their eyes increase in size as internal pressure builds up. When the eels move into sea water, its greater density offsets the increased blood pressure. The migration habits of two fishes, one a marine species entering fresh waters to spawn, the other a freshwater species going to the sea to spawn, have been studied in great detail. These are the Atlantic salmon and the freshwater eel.

The migration of *salmon* is far more than a trip from the sea to any accessible river where spawning can take place in fresh water. It involves a remarkable homing instinct, a stubborn determination to return to the exact place where the fish was born, no matter how small a tributary stream or pond

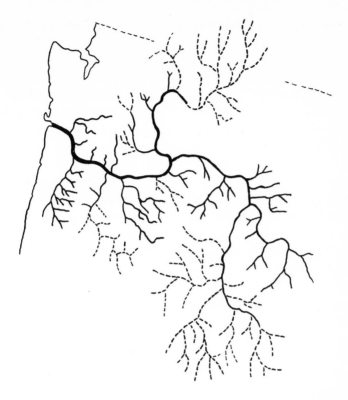

Spawning areas of Pacific salmon and trout in the Columbia River Basin. The solid lines indicate present available spawning areas; the dotted lines indicate former spawning areas now unavailable because of manmade conditions.

this may be. Some Alaskan salmon are known to travel 2000 miles from the sea up the Yukon River, swimming upstream against tremendous obstacles to reach a specific spawning ground. This is done at the rate of 40 or 50 miles a day. The feat is even more amazing when one realizes that during the trip the salmon do not feed at all but subsist on the stored fat they accumulated while at sea. Salmon begin their trek in a plump and healthy condition. But, battered and thin, only the strongest reach their destination. There they spawn and, having spawned, they die. Why do salmon undertake this exhausting, long trip into fresh waters to spawn? No one knows for sure. One theory is that as spawning time approaches a salmon's metabolism is stepped up and there is a craving for more oxygen. The salmon ascend the rivers where the oxygen supply is greater than in the sea. According to another theory, salmon have an urge to enter fresh water because of the increasing buoyancy of the fat stored up while at sea. This leads to another question: how do the salmon find their way? The answer to this also is not yet definitely known. Experiments seem to prove that a salmon may have a chemical sense enabling it to detect its home waters. But regardless of what science may in the future discover, the endurance, the singleness of purpose, the navigational skill demonstrated by spawning salmon remain the most remarkable feats of the animal world.

The migration of the *freshwater eels* of eastern North America and western Europe is not only another example of unusual spawning habits but also an intriguing detective story. The mystery is, "Where are the freshwater eels born?" The investigators are the ichthyologists of many different countries who pooled their efforts in tracking down the answer. Neither the American eel nor its close relative in Europe ever reproduces in the streams and ponds where they spend most of their lives. The mature eels go down to the sea and there disappear. Every year a new generation of young eels, known as elvers, appears near shore and enters the streams and ponds. Where do the mature eels go and where have the young eels come from?

It is difficult to track the departing eels through the thousands of square miles in the vast North Atlantic Ocean. But a clue came to light with the discovery of a strange, small, ribbonlike, and transparent fish that was named a leptocephalus. After many years of research, these were found to be the larval stage of the eel, just as a tadpole is the larval stage of a frog. The search now narrowed down to finding out where the leptocephalus came from. Ichthyologists patiently collected specimens of the eel larvae from many different locations in the Atlantic Ocean and found that they grew smaller and smaller as one approached the Sargasso Sea. Finally, the birthplace of the leptocephalus was pinpointed at a spot southeast of Bermuda for the European species, and a nearby region north of the West Indies for the American eel. In this part of the North Atlantic the eggs are laid, hatching in late winter or early spring and growing into quarter-inch larvae that drift northward with the Gulf Stream.

The larvae of the American eel reach the northeastern coast of the United States in the autumn of their first year. That winter they become transformed into elvers that can swim like adult eels and so travel up the streams. The larvae of the European eel have a longer trip, and it takes them three years to drift to Europe. Their growth is slower than that of the American leptocephalus so that they become elvers soon after arrival off the European coast. For this species it is after the third summer that the young elvers enter the streams to live. In both species, the males remain in the brackish waters around the river mouths, but the females swim farther upstream into the headwaters and ponds. The hordes of migrating elvers form swarms of wriggling fishes that bypass waterfalls and rapids and even travel overland in the wet grass when necessary. The females, which grow to twice the size of the males, live in their freshwater homes for a period of from five to twenty years. As they mature, their bodies darken, they lose their appetite, and begin their return downstream. Both male and female eels then go out to sea following the urge to retrace their course to a birthplace thousands of miles away in the trackless depths of the ocean. After a trip that takes several months, for eels swim very slowly, they reach their ancestral spawning grounds, produce young—and die.

The next time you hook a squirming eel and throw the slippery fish, perhaps in disgust, back into the water, take a moment to look with respect at an animal born far from the

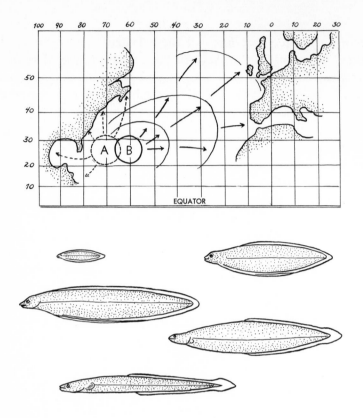

The life history of the freshwater eel. Map of the North At-lantic Ocean shows (A) spawning ground of the American eel and (B) that of the European eel. The dotted line is the path of the young eels to their American homes, the solid lines and arrows that of the European eels. Lower figures show the changes taking place in the growth of leptocephali into elvers.

pond where you found it, destined when full grown to take a trip longer than most of us will ever take—and far more hazardous. All of this is done without benefit of compass or engines, simply by the use of living energy in such a seemingly uncomplicated animal as an eel.

The Atlantic salmon, a typical member of the Salmon Family, is a prized game fish of northeastern North America; it bears the adipose fin on the back, in front of the tail fin.
American Museum of Natural History, New York

Chapter Three

Freshwater Game Fishes

Every reader has, no doubt, as a child caught a sunfish or a perch with a rusty hook and a worm. For many Americans a vacation or a camping trip is merely an excuse to go fishing. Millions of adults with expensive equipment pit their skill against that of a leaping salmon or a fighting bass. Thus many people already have some firsthand knowledge of the common fishes that live in our streams and lakes. We shall enlarge upon this acquaintance and also introduce species or describe aspects of their private lives that may be less familiar. Few countries are as fortunate as the United States in the wealth of game and food fishes that abounds in its many and varied freshwater habitats. These range from the rushing ice-cold brooks of the Pacific Northwest to the sluggish bayous of the lower Mississippi River valley. Streams teeming with fishes drain into the sea along the thousands of miles of both the Atlantic and Pacific coasts. The great rivers of the central United States form a network of waterways that are the homes of many different kinds of fishes. The Great Lakes form a vast reservoir filled with many other kinds of fishes, as do the many ponds and lakes that dot the landscape from New England and Wisconsin to the Gulf of Mexico. We cannot meet all the species that live in these varied habitats, but we can form a nodding acquaintance with the families of fishes represented in our inland waters.

Table 5. Rod-and-Reel Freshwater World Records

Species	Weight (in pounds and ounces)	Length (in inches)	Where Caught
Bass, Largemouth	22– 4	32	Georgia
Bass, Smallmouth	11–15	27	Kentucky
Bullhead, Black	8	24	New York
Bluegill Sunfish	4–12	15	Alabama
Carp	55– 5	42	Minnesota
Catfish, Blue	97	57	South Dakota
Catfish, Channel	57	44	South Carolina
Crappie, Black	5	19	South Carolina
Gar, Alligator	279	93	Texas
Muskellunge	69–15	64	New York
Perch, White	4–12	19	Maine
Perch, Yellow	4– 3	–	New Jersey
Pickerel, Eastern	9– 6	31	Georgia
Pike, Northern	46– 2	52	New York
Salmon, Atlantic	79– 2	–	Norway
Salmon, Chinook	92	58	British Columbia
Salmon, Landlocked	22– 8	36	Maine
Sturgeon, White	360	111	Idaho
Trout, Brook	14– 8	31	Ontario
Trout, Brown	39– 8	–	Scotland
Trout, Lake	63– 2	51	Lake Superior
Trout, Rainbow	37	40	Idaho

The common freshwater game and food fishes belong to six families. Three of these include soft-rayed fishes, having a single dorsal fin without spines: the salmon, catfish, and pike families. Three include spiny-rayed fishes, with the dorsal fin divided into a forward spiny portion and a soft-rayed posterior portion: the sunfish, perch, and sea bass families. The *Salmon Family* can be recognized by the streamlined body, four times

70

as long as deep, and by the presence of an adipose fin behind the dorsal fin. The *Catfish Family* is like the salmon family in having an adipose fin, but the body is flattened and often pudgy like that of other bottom-dwellers. Another distinctive feature is the presence of barbels around the mouth. The third soft-rayed family is the *Pike Family,* which lacks the adipose fin and is characterized by extremely long and slender bodies six or seven times as long as deep. Pikes and their relatives also have elongated, pointed snouts. The *Sunfish Family* includes many fishes with a stubby, compressed body flattened vertically, half as deep as it is long. In some species, such as bass, the body is about three times as long as deep. Members of this family have the spiny and soft-rayed portions of the fin united into a single dorsal fin. The *Perch Family* includes fishes with a more slender body and with the spiny portion of the dorsal fin separated from the soft-rayed, resulting in two dorsal fins. The *Sea Bass Family* includes several fresh-water species; they are chunky fishes with a body about three times as long as deep, and with the two parts of the dorsal fin close together—a condition intermediate between that of the sunfish and the perch families.

The Salmon Family

In the Salmon Family are found many well-known and valuable fishes; in addition to salmon and trout, it includes whitefish and cisco, both important food fishes of the Great Lakes region. Fishes in this family have graceful, elongated bodies covered with cycloid scales; the single dorsal fin is located near the middle of the back above the ventral fins, and the pectoral fins are set far forward. The large mouth is provided with sharp jaw teeth indicating the carnivorous habits of the species. The family includes over a hundred species, of which thirty occur in the United States. Salmon and trout, as we have learned already, are unusual in the care for the young exhibited by the parents during spawning.

Some species live their entire lives in fresh water, while others are marine species that migrate into streams to spawn. As the latter, which include many of our salmon and trout species, are game fishes during their migration inland, they will be considered with the other strictly freshwater members of the family.

ATLANTIC SALMON. Since the days of the Romans, men have considered this salmon, which occurs on both coasts of the North Atlantic Ocean, a prize game and food fish. The common and scientific names of salmon both come from the Latin word *salio* meaning "leap"—an appropriate name as anyone will agree who has watched this silvery beauty jumping out of the water. In western Europe, where their habitat has been carefully protected, Atlantic salmon are still abundant. Salmon were formerly plentiful throughout northeastern United States, but stream pollution, dams, and other modifications of the salmon's habitat practically have eliminated this colorful species from the United States. Migrating salmon can now be found in only a few coastal rivers of Maine, but they are still abundant in Nova Scotia and Newfoundland.

Fresh from the sea, Atlantic salmon are a glistening silver with a blue back marked with X-shaped spots. Spawning salmon become reddish brown, and the males develop elongated jaws with a prominent hook to the tip of the lower jaw. Some varieties of salmon have become landlocked, never returning to the sea; this is the case with the salmon in Sebago Lake, Maine. Such permanent freshwater dwellers become greenish brown marked with red and brown spots. Little is known of where and how the salmon live while in the sea. However, there they fatten and grow large on a diet of shrimp, crab, and other marine invertebrates, storing up energy for the long period of fasting during the spawning migration into the rivers. Plump, sea-run salmon—four or five years old—can be found in the streams from mid-May to mid-July; they grow to a length of 30 inches or more and weigh at least 10 pounds.

Smaller salmon, known as grilse, that have spent only one year at sea, weight 5 pounds or less. Many adults die after spawning; it has been estimated that only 15% of the fishes return to spawn a second time.

The salmon of the Pacific Coast belong to five different species; together they make up the most valuable freshwater food fish of North America. The salmon begin running in March and continue until spawning time from August to November. Some species are caught at all seasons. Pacific salmon often reveal striking differences between the sexes during the spawning season. The snout of the male becomes distorted, the upper jaw becomes hooked, and a fleshy hump may develop in front of the dorsal fin. In some species the silvery color changes to a brilliant red. The Pacific salmon generally die after spawning; unlike the Atlantic salmon they are rarely caught by hook in fresh water. The flesh is rich and red in spring when the well-fed salmon return from their feeding grounds in the sea. As the fishes reach the end of their spawning run, they lose weight and their flesh becomes dry and tasteless.

CHINOOK SALMON, also known as king salmon, is the largest species, averaging 10 to 20 pounds in weight, with some individuals attaining a record-breaking 100 pounds. A typical chinook salmon has silvery sides and bluish-green back marked with small dark spots; it occurs over a large range from California to Alaska. SOCKEYE SALMON, or red salmon, is found from Oregon to Alaska; the spawning males assume a colorful attire with a bright red body and a green head. The average sockeye salmon is 2 feet in length and weighs 3 to 5 pounds. A recent annual catch of these two valuable food species exceeded 100,000,000 pounds. COHO SALMON, or silver salmon, is another small species, usually under 5 pounds in weight; it has the same range as the chinook salmon. Coho salmon is abundant from Puget Sound to Alaska. PINK SALMON, also known as humpback salmon because of the appearance of the male during spawning, is

73

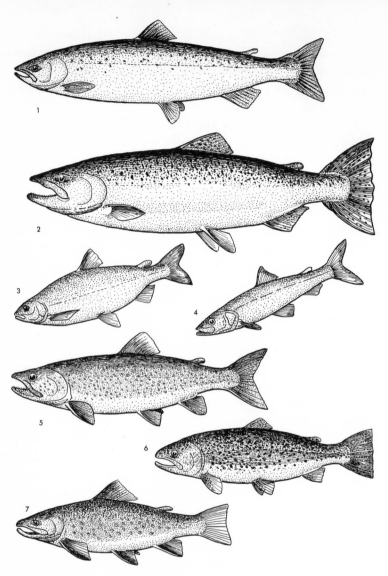

The Salmon Family includes well-known food and game fishes of fresh water: Atlantic salmon (1), chinook salmon (2), whitefish (3), cisco (4), lake trout (5), rainbow trout (6) and brook trout (7). Figures 1, 2, 5, 6, 7 adapted from Maynard Reece in Life Magazine; 3 and 4 from Francesca La Monte, "North American Game Fishes."

especially common in Alaska, although it occurs as far south as Oregon. It is usually between 3 and 6 pounds in weight. The flesh, somewhat inferior to that of sockeye or chinook, is canned as pink salmon.

Trout are without question the best-known American freshwater game fishes. There are ten different species, many of them so widely transplanted that today they are found in practically every state with suitable streams and lakes. Some trout are related closely to the Atlantic salmon; such are the rainbow, cutthroat, and brown trout. Rainbow and cutthroat trout sometimes migrate to the sea, returning to fresh water to spawn. Trout that do this are a silvery blue color on their return from the sea. Often they are called steelheads and are considered to be a separate species. However, a steelhead is merely a trout that recently has returned from the sea. Other familiar trout are the lake, brook, and Dolly Varden species.

The RAINBOW TROUT is so named because of its striking coloration. It has silvery and pink sides, a greenish back, and many small colored spots scattered over the body. This coloring is extremely variable, depending upon the age and sex of the trout and the environment in which it has been living. Its usual length is 8 to 20 inches, with a weight of from 2 to 8 pounds. A record specimen caught in an Idaho lake was 40 inches long and weighed 37 pounds. Originally found only on the Pacific Coast from California to Alaska, rainbows have now been widely introduced throughout the United States. This species can tolerate warmer and more quiet water than the brook trout; its preferred home is in streams and lakes. As in some salmon, during the breeding season the male becomes bright red. Spawning takes place in spring; the eggs hatch in a month, the young appearing during June and July.

CUTTHROAT TROUT is considered the parent type of all American trout. It gets its name from the bright red blotch beneath the lower jaw; otherwise it is silvery in color with golden tints along the sides and scattered spots, which are often larger than those of a rainbow. The cutthroat is found in cold mountain streams from California to Alaska. The average size is under 12 inches but some individuals reach a length of 36 inches and weigh up to 40 pounds. BROWN TROUT is a European species that was introduced into the United States over sixty years ago; it is now found from New England to California. It is able to survive in sluggish streams and small ponds; less sensitive to its surroundings than other trout, it can thrive in habitats where our native trout are unable to live. The coloration of a brown trout is usually yellowish brown with large dark spots, each surrounded by a lighter halo. It also has a silvery phase in which it easily can be mistaken for a landlocked salmon. The usual weight of a brown trout ranges from 3 to 10 pounds; a large one may weigh as much as 30 pounds.

LAKE TROUT is the largest of the trouts and, as the name implies, is an inhabitant of ponds, and lakes. It occurs from New England, where it is known as togue, across northern United States to Alaska. Lake trout prefer cool deep water but come to the surface for sunning and inshore for feeding. They have an omnivorous appetite, greedily eating anything from leaves and trash to smelts, eels, and even small birds. Lake trout is variable in color but commonly is brownish or greenish gray with silvery sides and numerous light spots scattered over the darker gray background. Most trout have a square-cut tail but that of the lake trout is forked. Lake trout are usually 20 to 30 inches in length and weigh under 10 pounds; specimens of record size reach a weight of 60 pounds. In the Great Lakes this species was of considerable commercial value, with an annual catch of millions of pounds; the trout population has been reduced greatly since the invasion of these lakes by the parasitic lampreys (see p. 207). Lake trout spawn in shallow water from October to November; unlike their relatives, this species constructs no nest and exhibits no parental care of the young. The eggs are fertilized haphazardly and scattered over the bottom, hatching in five months.

The BROOK TROUT is an olive or yellowish brown fish marked by lighter spots and occasional red dots. It is usually 7 to 16 inches in length with an average weight of 2 pounds, although large individuals weighing as much as 10 pounds frequently are caught. This species originally was found only in the northern portion of the United States east of the Mississippi River; now it is widespread as a result of artificial propagation, being found west to the Pacific Coast. Spawning occurs from September to December, the eggs hatching in three months. Brook trout are voracious feeders, devouring chiefly small fishes such as smelt but also eating insects, mollusks, and crustaceans.

DOLLY VARDEN TROUT is a native of the Pacific Coast. It resembles a brook trout but is more slender, lacks the dark markings, and the tail fin is forked slightly. Dolly Varden is common in streams but periodically migrates to the sea. When it returns as a sea-run trout, it is silvery, as are other members of the trout and salmon group upon their return from the ocean. The usual size is 8 to 20 inches, and the weight ranges from 2 pounds for those found in streams to 20 pounds for those in lakes. Dolly Varden is not very popular with fishermen because it feeds on the eggs and young of other trout species.

The Salmon Family includes two species which are more important as food than as game. WHITEFISH is a green and silvery fish with a purplish iridescence and with a deeply forked tail fin. Whitefish has larger scales and a smaller mouth than salmon or trout; the mouth lacks teeth or else has very weak ones. The usual size is from 2 to 4 pounds in weight and under 16 inches in length. Whitefish lives in deep, large lakes from Maine to the Great Lakes, and it feeds on insects and mollusks as well as smaller fishes. The largest commercial catch is taken in Lake Michigan. Whitefish displays no nesting habits and no care of the young. CISCO, or lake herring, is another important Great Lakes fish with an annual catch also running into the millions of pounds. Cisco is a pale green or bluish fish with silvery sides; a typical one weighs about 2 pounds. This fish is chiefly a bottom-feeder, eating crustaceans and insects.

The Catfish Family

In the United States, members of the freshwater Catfish Family number about twenty-four species and are found for the most part in the rivers and lakes of the Mississippi River valley; no species are native to the Pacific Coast. The family includes, in addition to catfishes, the smaller bullheads, madtoms, and stonecats. These are unusual in lacking scales and having long barbels on the head, which give the fish a cat-like resemblance. The head is broad and rounded, the mouth large, and the jaws contain small conical teeth. A single dorsal fin is located well forward on the back, and an adipose fin is situated in front of the tail fin as in the salmon family. Catfishes are greedy and omnivorous feeders on anything they can grub from the bottom; their favorite diet consists of insects and their larvae, and other small aquatic invertebrates, In spite of an unprepossessing appearance, catfish are good eating, with firm flaky flesh.

The BLUE CATFISH is the largest member of the family. Formerly large individuals weighing up to 100 pounds were caught, but today one 5 feet in length and weighing 30 pounds is considered a large specimen. The blue "cat" is a fish of the streams, ponds, and bayous of the lower Mississippi River valley and Gulf states. As the name suggests, it is a slaty blue fish; the sides are silvery and unspotted. The FLATHEAD CATFISH is also a large species, growing to a length of 4 or 5 feet and 50 pounds or more in weight. The head is flattened and the adipose fin is very large; the tail fin is only slightly forked in contrast with the deeply forked tail fin of the blue catfish. This species is known also as the yellow "cat" because of its yellowish brown color, and as the

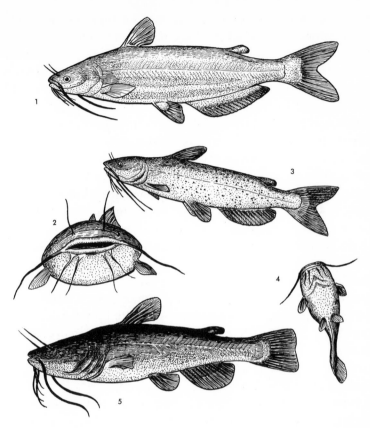

The Catfish Family includes the blue catfish (1, 2), channel catfish (3), brown bullhead (4) and black bullhead (5). Figures 1, 2, 3 adapted from Maynard Reece in Life Magazine, 4 from Hashime Murayama in National Geographic Magazine.

mud catfish because of its preference for the bottom of muddy streams. It, too, is common in the lower Mississippi River valley.

The CHANNEL CATFISH is a slaty gray fish with silvery sides, differing from the blue catfish in having an olive-brown back and spots on the sides. This catfish prefers the clear, cool water of streams with considerable current, and

79

also large lakes. It feeds on insects, crayfish, mussels, and small fishes. An average individual is 2 feet long and weighs about 5 pounds; a very large size is 4 feet and 50 pounds. Channel catfish are found from New York south and west to Florida and the Gulf of Mexico. Smallest species is the WHITE CATFISH, also called horned pout and Potomac "cat"; it is found in rivers, lakes, and brackish estuaries from Maryland to Texas. This species also has been introduced into California. A white catfish is gray or silvery blue with a greenish tinge and has a deeply forked tail. Commonly about 2 feet in length, it is a scavenging species with very large head and a wide mouth. White catfish is the species marketed commercially.

Bullheads are smaller members of the family, with a square-cut or rounded tail fin. The BROWN BULLHEAD, or common bullhead, has a wide range in sluggish streams and weedy ponds from New England to central United States and south to Texas. It is a mottled greenish brown fish usually under 12 inches in length and seldom weighs more than a pound or two. Brown bullheads feed on bottom-dwelling snails, crayfish, and insects. This species has been introduced into California where it may be found at times in brackish water. The YELLOW BULLHEAD is a yellowish brown species of sluggish waters from New York and the Great Lakes south to Texas. It has the same size and living habits as the brown bullhead. Smallest of the common species is the BLACK BULLHEAD, found in brooks and ponds from New York westward. Its coloring is a dark olive-green to a dusky black; a distinctive white bar marks the base of the slightly forked tail fin.

STONECATS are small members of the family, less than 12 inches in length. They are found in creeks and rivers of central and western United States. An unusual feature, as noted in a previous chapter, is a poison gland at the base of the pectoral spines. Relatives of the stonecats known as MAD-TOMS can easily be mistaken for oversized tadpoles.

The Pike Family

This is a group of Arctic fishes common to northern Europe and North America; our native species are well-known game fishes of the Great Lakes region. Pikes and their relatives the pickerels and muskellunge have long slender bodies terminating in a sharply pointed head; the large mouth is well armed with teeth in the jaws, on the roof of the mouth, and on the tongue. A short dorsal fin is set far back on the body above the ventral fins; the body is covered with cycloid scales that have deeply scalloped margins. They are all voracious carnivores that have been deservedly called "freshwater pirates." They devour not only other fishes but also muskrats, mice, frogs, and even ducklings. Using submerged vegetation and stumps as lurking places, they dart out suddenly to capture their prey.

Smallest member of the family is the **REDFIN PICKEREL**, or barred pickerel, found east of the Allegheny Mountains from Maine to Florida in small streams and brooks. It is rarely more than 12 inches in length and 1 pound in weight. In color it is a dusky green with dark curved bars along the sides; as the name implies, the fins have a reddish tinge. The **EASTERN PICKEREL**, also known as chain pickerel, is a larger species, 15 to 24 inches in length and reaching a weight of 9 pounds. It is a golden-green fish marked by a network of dark lines. Eastern pickerel inhabits clear, grassy ponds and lakes from northern New England to Florida. This species is a greedy eater of frogs and small fishes. The adults lead solitary lives, poised motionless and well camouflaged amid the aquatic vegetation as they wait for an unwary minnow or perch.

NORTHERN PIKE, or great northern pickerel, is an olive-green fish with horizontal markings of a lighter color and a yellowish or white belly. The head when viewed from above bears a remarkable resemblance to a duck's bill. The northern pike lives in sluggish streams and weedy lakes from

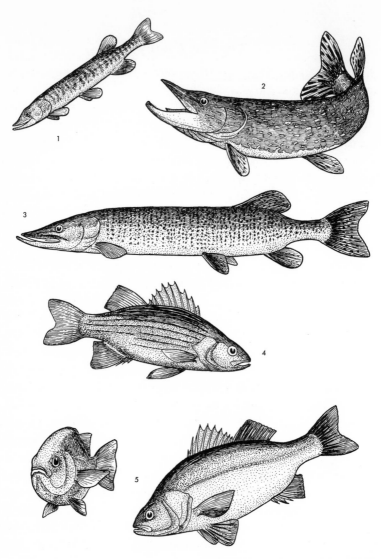

The Pike Family includes the redfin pickerel (1), northern pike (2), and muskellunge (3). The Sea Bass Family has such fresh-water members as white bass (4) and white perch (5). Figures 1 and 3 adapted from Maynard Reece in Life Magazine; 5 from Hashime Murayama and 2 and 4 from Walter Weber in National Geographic Magazine.

New England across the continent to Alaska. An average individual ranges in length from 20 to 40 inches, and the maximum weight is 40 pounds. It spawns in early spring, usually along grassy stream margins. The eggs, which adhere to the water weeds, hatch in two weeks; the young feed on water fleas and other insects, later on newly hatched minnows and suckers. Adults feed on insects, leeches, and other fishes.

Giant of the family is the MUSKELLUNGE, or great pike, found in the Great Lakes and in Canada. Muskellunge is one of the largest freshwater game fishes, with a length ranging from 30 to 50 inches and a weight of up to 50 pounds. Individuals of record size may be 5 feet in length and weigh as much as 69 pounds. It is an olive or brownish fish with faint vertical markings on the sides and spotted fins. Muskellunge is a highly prized trophy, equaling the barracuda in its fierceness when hooked. "Muskies" lead solitary lives in cool, clear water where they prey on other fishes, snakes, and frogs.

The Sunfish Family

This is an exclusively North American group of fishes, with some thirty common species in streams and ponds; the great majority are found in the eastern United States. The family can be recognized by the ctenoid scales; the dorsal fin, which has a spiny forward portion; and the position of the ventral fins, which are far forward beneath the pectoral fins. Members of the family vary in gaminess from the easily caught pumpkinseed, joy of every youthful fisherman, to the smallmouth bass, which is considered the best sports fish for its size in the country. All species in the family are spring spawners, and many, as indicated in a previous chapter, reveal surprising parental care in making nests and guarding the young. The newly hatched fishes feed on plankton and small aquatic invertebrates; the adults are carnivorous and feed mainly on other smaller fishes. Three groups comprise the sunfish family: the sunfishes (which include rock bass and Sacramento perch), the smallmouth and largemouth bass, and the crappies.

Sunfishes are small colorful fishes, often exceedingly thin when viewed head-on. They can be recognized by a prolongation of the gill cover to form a flap or "ear." The PUMPKINSEED, also known as redbelly and pond perch, inhabits weedy ponds and streams throughout eastern United States. It has been introduced also into the western states. The pumpkinseed is a brightly colored fish with mottled yellow and brown sides, a bright red spot on the edge of the gill flap, and occasionally with a blue stripe across the cheek. It is usually 7 to 10 inches in length and rarely weighs as much as 1 pound. Its food consists of bottom-dwelling crustaceans, insects, and snails. The REDBREAST, or yellowbelly, thrives in lakes with dense bottom vegetation; although found from Maine to Florida, it prefers the warmer lakes south of New York. This sunfish, olive-green and unspotted, has a rosy-red belly; it is slightly longer and thinner than the pumpkinseed, and the elongated ear flap is entirely black. The GREEN SUNFISH, of the same general size, frequents sluggish creeks and small ponds from the Atlantic Coast to the Rockies and has been introduced into California. This is an olive-green fish with faint vertical bars and a red-rimmed black ear flap. The BLUEGILL, sometimes known as the blue bream, is the largest of our sunfishes, at times reaching a length of 12 inches and a weight slightly over 1 pound. The largest bluegill ever caught was 15 inches long and weighed 4 pounds. It is brownish green with reddish sides, marked by faint vertical bars and with an orange-red breast; the ear flaps are blue tipped with black. The bluegill sunfish prefers ponds and quiet streams with a dense bottom growth of plants where it can feed on insects, crustaceans, and smaller fishes. This species, native to the eastern United States, has been introduced into the Sacramento–San Joaquin region of California.

ROCK BASS, also known as rock sunfish or redeye, is an olive-green or brown fish with mottled markings and a dis-

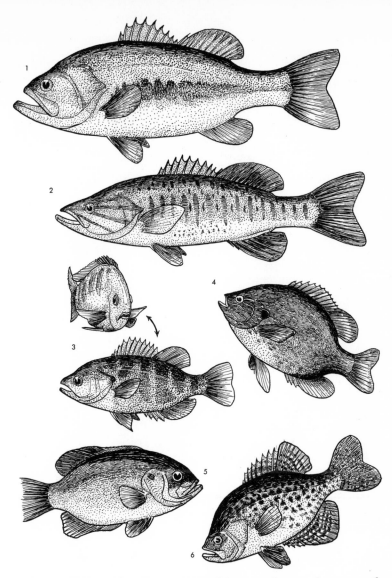

The Sunfish Family has such familiar members as largemouth (1) and smallmouth (2) black bass, Sacramento perch (3), pumpkinseed sunfish (4), black rock bass (5) and black crappie (6). Figures 1, 2, and 3 adapted from Maynard Reece in Life Magazine; 4 from Walter Weber and 5, 6 from Hashime Murayama in National Geographic Magazine.

tinctive red eye. It lives in reedy lakes and streams from the Great Lakes southward. Some individuals attain a weight of 2 pounds. SACRAMENTO PERCH is a native of the Sacramento River region of California, the only member of the family native to the Pacific Coast. Sacramento perch varies in color from silvery white to black; its average size ranges from 8 to 12 inches. Unlike its relatives, this species exhibits no nest building activity and no care of the young.

The two best-known game fishes of the family are smallmouth bass and largemouth bass. SMALLMOUTH BASS is also known as tiger bass, black bass, and brown bass; its reputation as a game fish is unsurpassed by any other freshwater fish its size. From its original home in the St. Lawrence, Ohio, and upper Mississippi River valleys, the smallmouth bass has been introduced widely from Maine to Florida. The body is longer and not so thin as that of the sunfishes; the upper jaw extends back only to a point below the eye. The color is a dark greenish brown above, a lighter shade on the sides, with irregular dark markings. This bass is usually 10 to 20 inches in length and less than 8 pounds in weight. A record size is 27 inches and 11 pounds. The smallmouth bass prefers flowing streams and cool, clear lakes with gravelly shorelines. Here it feeds on insects, crayfishes, and other smaller fishes.

The LARGEMOUTH BASS also goes by a number of other names: green bass, marsh bass, and bayou bass. This is an olive-green fish, often marked by a dark longitudinal stripe along the side. The jaw extends backward beyond the eye, hence the common name. A native of the Great Lakes and Mississippi River region, this species has now been introduced into many other states including those on the Pacific Coast. It prefers warmer waters than does the smallmouth and thus is found more frequently in sluggish streams and weedy ponds. It is the largest member of the sunfish family; an average individual is 12 to 24 inches in length, and some have been caught up to 32 inches and weighing 22 pounds. The largemouth feeds mainly on other fishes, its maximum size depending upon how much of this food is available. The spawning habits are similar to those of the smallmouth. The eggs hatch in seven to ten weeks, the time varying with the temperature of the water.

Crappies are chunky, basslike fishes greenish or olive-brown in color and distinctively barred. In profile, the back slopes down suddenly to the head, which projects into a snout. The BLACK CRAPPIE, or calico bass, is a small fish usually under 8 inches in length and rarely weighing over 2 pounds. Maximum size and weight for this species is 19 inches and 5 pounds. The black crappie is a fish of streams and lakes with abundant vegetation amid which it feeds on insects and their larvae, and minnows. Black crappies are found from the Great Lakes south to New Jersey and southwest to Texas. The WHITE CRAPPIE, of the same size and habits, is a lighter-colored fish with more irregular markings, common in streams and lakes from the Mississippi River to the Rocky Mountains. Both species have been introduced into California.

The Perch Family

In this group of freshwater fishes, unlike the sunfish family, the two portions of the dorsal fin are separated from each other. The perch family is a large one, with over a hundred species in the United States. Three types of fishes are included in the family: the yellow perch, the pike perches, and the darters. The first two inhabit streams and lakes and are found in Europe as well as in North America. The darters, which make up the greatest number of species in the family, are found only in streams in North America.

YELLOW PERCH, also known as red perch or striped perch, is a familiar fish of central and eastern United States; it has been introduced also on the Pacific Coast. The first dorsal fin bears very strong spines. Viewed from the side, the head is somewhat concave above the eyes, and the body is

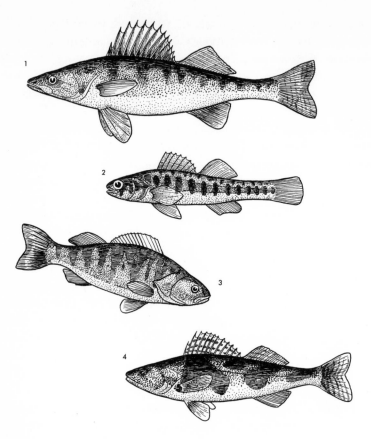

The Perch Family includes walleye (1), Iowa darter (2), yellow perch (3), and sauger (4). Figures 1 and 4 adapted from Maynard Reece in Life Magazine, 3 from Walter Weber in National Geographic Magazine, 2 from Hubbs and Lagler, "Fishes of the Great Lakes Region."

humped in front of the dorsal fin. Yellow perch is, as the name suggests, a yellowish green in color; there are several dark vertical bars on the sides, the back is dark green, and the pectoral fins have a yellow tinge. As in the sunfish family, the ventral fins are located almost directly beneath the pectorals. A yellow perch is usually 8 to 14 inches in length and weighs less than 2 pounds; 4 pounds is a maximum size. This species prefers quiet streams and ponds where it can find an ample supply of worms, insects, crustaceans, and other small aquatic animals. Yellow perch spawn in spring near shore. The eggs are laid in zigzag gelatinous strings several feet in length that swell upon contact with the water and become entangled with the stems of aquatic plants.

The SAUGER or sand pike is a longer and more slender fish, but it has the same olive-green coloring and yellowish sides. The markings are irregular dark blotches rather than vertical bars. The dorsal fin is also spotted. The sauger is ordinarily under 12 inches in length and rarely weighs as much as 2 pounds. It is found in large lakes from Canada to West Virginia and Tennessee but is most abundant in Lake Erie. The WALLEYE, yellow pike perch, or walleyed pike is a common Great Lakes fish. This is the largest member of the perch family, averaging 10 to 20 inches in length, exceptional specimens reaching 30 inches and a weight of 20 pounds. The walleye is olive-green and yellowish with indistinct dark markings. The lower jaw is armed with long front teeth, lacking in the yellow perch. Walleyes live in deep clear lakes; they are powerful and swift swimmers capable of catching bass and perch as well as sunfishes and minnows. In Lake Erie, where they are abundant, they rank in commercial importance with whitefish and lake trout. The walleye makes no nest and exhibits no parental care; it spawns in spring, and the eggs settle to the bottom among the water plants, hatching in two or three weeks.

Darters are small minnowlike fishes two or three inches in length. The MUD DARTER, common along the Atlantic and Gulf coasts, is a species of slow-flowing and muddy streams. It lacks an air bladder and as a result spends its life resting on the bottom among the water weeds. This species and its relatives have the habit of suddenly darting out after their prey. The IOWA DARTER is a more colorful fish, common in the Great Lakes region. The dorsal fin is orange and black, the underside is yellowish, and a conspicuous brown streak extends along the side. Some darters exhibit considerable parental care; the males excavate nests between stones and other bottom debris and guard the eggs while they are hatching.

The Sea Bass Family

Although most members of this family are marine fishes, several species live in rivers and lakes; they are the white bass, yellow bass, and white perch. WHITE BASS inhabits deep, quiet water over sandy or gravelly bottom, typically found in large lakes and deep rivers. It occurs in the Great Lakes region and ranges southward to Texas. In profile, a white bass reveals a concave outline above the eyes and a hump in front of the spiny fin. The lower jaw projects pugnaciously. White bass is a metallic silver-and-gold color with indefinite horizontal stripes along the upper sides. The ventral fins are situated well forward, only slightly behind the pectoral fins. Individuals have been caught that measured 18 inches in length and weighed as much as 3 pounds. YELLOW BASS is a more southern species with more distinct horizontal stripes on the yellowish green body. It grows to the same size as the white bass and is common from the Great Lakes to the lower Mississippi River region. WHITE PERCH, found from New England to South Carolina, is a saltwater fish that enters fresh waters to spawn and often becomes landlocked. It is a silvery fish with bluish back and without the stripes found in other members of the family. An average specimen is 15 inches or less in length and under 2 pounds in weight. White perch seeks tributary streams and shallows for spawning during May and June. No nest is made, and no parental care is shown; the adhesive eggs sink to the bottom and stick to submerged rocks and grasses. This member of the sea-bass family formerly was an important commercial catch in the Chesapeake Bay region.

A school of minnows, also known as shiners, swims through a
submarine field of waterweeds at Silver Springs, Florida.
Mozert of Silver Springs

Chapter Four

Some Other Freshwater Fishes

Streams and ponds are the homes of many kinds of fishes other than those that interest the sport fisherman. Among these, which usually are not considered game fishes, are about a dozen families; some are an essential part of the food chain, serving as forage for the larger game fishes; others have unusual life histories or breeding habits; still others represent primitive or unusual types of fishes that are often called "living fossils."

The schools of small silvery fishes that dart about in shallow water includes species of the common *Minnow Family* and *Killifish Family*. These form the bulk of the diet of the large carnivorous fishes. In the same way, the young of the bottom-dwelling *Sucker Family* are food for the more valuable game fishes. Unusual life histories and reproductive habits are typical of three families: the *Freshwater Eel Family,* the *Stickleback Family,* and the *Live-bearer Family.* The long migration of freshwater eels to the Sargasso Sea, the birdlike nests constructed by the sticklebacks, the mammal-like habit of the live-bearers in giving birth to living young—all are fascinating aspects of life beneath the surface of our ponds and streams. Of special interest are those fishes that retain a primitive body and so are "hold-overs" from a previous geologic era when fishes were beginning their evolution. The *Sturgeon Family* consists of armored fishes that are giants among their freshwater neighbors. The *Gar Family* includes other large and primitive predators of freshwater habitats. And no excursion into the depths of a pond or a river would be complete without mention of the strange *Bowfin Family* and *Paddlefish Family*.

The Minnow Family

In popular language any small fish is a minnow. True minnows, however, are particular species belonging to the Minnow Family. This is one of the largest groups of fishes, with almost two hundred species in the United States alone. Its representatives live in various kinds of freshwater habitats throughout the north temperate zone. Minnows are soft-rayed fishes with cycloid scales, a single dorsal fin, and a forked tail fin. The jaws are toothless, but pharyngeal teeth in the throat assist in grinding and masticating food, which consists mainly of small aquatic animals such as insects and their larvae, crustaceans, and mollusks. Many members of the family are small, and some exhibit a rainbow variety of colors. The common aquarium goldfish is a minnow, as are the much larger fallfish and squawfish. Minnows vary in their breeding habits, some broadcasting their eggs in a haphazard fashion, others burying them carefully or laying them in nests.

The COMMON MINNOW, or silver shiner, is a very familiar species found throughout eastern and central United States. The size ranges from 2 to 5 inches, but larger individuals are sometimes caught. During the spawning season the male develops rosy tints on the belly and lower fins and small spiny outgrowths on the head. The chief use of minnows is for bait. The REDSIDE DACE, about 4 inches in length, is a colorful minnow found in clear streams throughout southeastern United States. In spring the male becomes bright crimson on the forward portion of the body and also

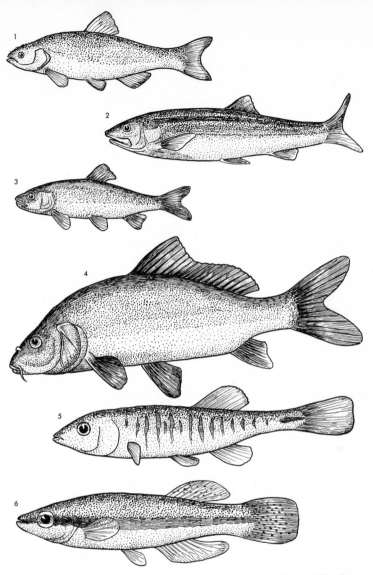

The Minnow Family includes the common shiner (1), Sacramento squawfish (2), fallfish (3), and carp (4). The Killifish Family includes the banded killifish (5) and blackstripe topminnow (6). Figures 3 and 4 adapted from Francesca La Monte "North American Game Fishes"; 2 from Hashime Murayama in National Geographic Magazine; 5 and 6 from Hubbs and Lagler, "Fishes of the Great Lakes Region."

develops many small tubercles. Redside dace is often sold as an aquarium fish. The REDBELLY DACE, a small species only a few inches in length, is rated as the most handsome of all minnow species. It is a brownish fish with black spots on the back, two dark stripes along the side, and a bright red belly. The CUTLIP MINNOW has a peculiar three-lobed lower lip. It is a sluggish, fairly large species growing to a length of 8 inches, olive-green in color with a dusky bar behind the gill cover. Cutlip minnows live in the streams of eastern United States. The male constructs a nest of carefully selected pebbles that he moves to the site, usually beneath an overhanging rock. Here the eggs are laid, and the young develop in comparative safety.

FALLFISH, or silver chub, is one of the larger members of the minnow family, growing to a length of 18 inches. It is found in swift streams and clear lakes from New England to Virginia. Fallfish is a silvery species with a bluish back and a small barbel on the upper lip. It feeds on algae, crayfish, insects, and small fishes. The male builds a nest by collecting stones, some of which are an inch or two in size, and arranging them in a pile several feet high and five feet in diameter. The SACRAMENTO SQUAWFISH, or Sacramento pike, inhabits rivers in California and Oregon. It is a silvery fish with brownish green back and reddish fins. It grows even larger than the fallfish, reaching a length of 48 inches and a weight of 10 pounds. A related species in the Colorado River is said to weight as much as 80 pounds. Squawfish is a voracious species that consumes great numbers of the eggs and young of game fishes such as trout. As a result it is considered a menace in game fish areas.

CARP is another giant-sized member of the minnow group, native to Asia. It was introduced into the United States in 1877 and has since multiplied so rapidly as to become a nuisance in many game-fish ponds. Carp varies in color, being brassy or silvery in clear ponds, brownish green in muddy waters. Distinctive carp features are the long dorsal fin that tapers to the rear, and the presence of four barbels beneath the mouth. Carp is a hardy fish able to live in warm and polluted water where most native species cannot survive. They are omnivorous and greedy feeders, consuming great quantities of beetles, worms, and other invertebrates found in the mud, as well as algae and parts of water weeds. As they prowl along the bottom sucking in mouthfuls of mud and ejecting it again, carp succeed in roiling up the water much as pigs root up a pasture. Carp matures at the age of 3 years, when it is about 16 inches long; old individuals may be 36 inches long and weigh as much as 25 pounds. Carp spawn in reedy shallows, the females splashing the water vigorously as the eggs are laid; in this way the eggs become attached to the plants rather than sink into the mud where they might die from lack of air. In winter, carp become less active and settle into the mud where they remain without feeding until spring. This is the nearest approach to hiberation in the fish world.

GOLDFISH is a relative of the carp and is also a native of Asia. In the wild state, it is a greenish brown fish lacking the barbels of the carp but possessing the same elongated dorsal fin. Because of having been bred by the Chinese for centuries, many strange varieties of goldfish have been produced, as any aquarium enthusiast knows. Goldfishes have been introduced into park ponds and some rivers, where they thrive but eventually revert to their greenish brown color and grow to a much larger size. Such semiwild goldfishes are abundant in the Potomac River.

The Killifish Family

This family of small minnowlike fishes is represented by some 46 species in the United States and many others in tropical America, Africa, and Asia. American killifishes reach their greatest abundance in Florida and neighboring states. Like the minnows, the killifishes have a single soft-rayed dorsal fin and cycloid scales. They differ in having a flattened head, a mouth opening on the upper surface of the head (an adaptation for surface feeding), the dorsal fin set farther back near the tail, and a square-cut or rounded margin on the tail fin.

The BANDED KILLIFISH is a silvery species with dark vertical stripes; its average length is only 2 or 3 inches. This species lives in quiet bays as well as streams of central and eastern United States. The COMMON KILLIFISH, or mummichog, is also a small fish, under 5 inches in length, but surprisingly voracious for its size. It lives in weedy and muddy ponds from New England to the Gulf of Mexico. The females are a brownish green with lighter sides and underparts; the males are silvery on the sides with yellowish belly and fins. Both sexes are marked by narrow vertical bars. This is a hardy species capable of surviving in stagnant and polluted water; like carp, it buries itself in the mud for the winter. The STRIPED KILLIFISH, a larger fish up to 8 inches in length, is found in bays and river mouths along the Atlantic Coast from southern New England to Florida. This species reveals a difference in the appearance of the sexes; in the male the belly and fins are yellow and the sides are vertically barred, and in the female the underparts are more silvery and the sides are marked by longitudinal stripes. The BLACK STRIPE TOPMINNOW, about 2 inches in length, is a colorful member of the family, inhabiting quiet lakes and ponds of central United States. It is a yellowish fish with a silvery belly and sides marked by a conspicuous dark brown stripe extending from mouth to tail.

The Sucker Family

The Sucker Family includes one hundred species found for the most part in eastern and central United States. In some parts of the country they are considered game fishes, in others they are caught for food. In many game fish areas, the adult suckers overpopulate the lakes at the expense of other more desirable fishes and thus create a problem in fish conservation. Suckers are chiefly bottom-dwelling fishes closely related to the minnows in structural features. The body is covered with smooth cycloid scales, the tail fin is forked, and the dorsal fin lacks spines. The jaws are toothless, but pharyngeal teeth aid in eating. A special feature is the extendible mouth on the lower side of the head with fleshy lips that are useful in bottom feeding. Suckers live in ponds and streams, scouring the bottom like animated vacuum cleaners as they suck in diatoms, worms, snails, and other bits of aquatic life that coat the submerged stones and vegetation. They are among the few groups of fishes which are herbivorous as well as carnivorous.

The COMMON SUCKER, or white sucker, is abundant throughout the United States from New England and Florida to the Rocky Mountains. It is an olive-green or light brown fish, but the male assumes a rosy hue in spring. A sucker is usually 12 to 14 inches long and weighs between 3 and 5 pounds. In spring great numbers of suckers migrate into the smaller streams to spawn; they exhibit no nest-making activity nor any parental care. Coastal streams of western United States are the home of the SACRAMENTO SUCKER, an olive-brown fish with silvery sides. This species, with habits similar to those of its eastern relative, is usually under 24 inches in length and less than 2 pounds in weight. The LONGNOSE SUCKER, averaging 2 pounds in weight, is caught as a food fish in the Great Lakes, but its range extends eastward to the St. Lawrence River and westward to the Columbia River. Longnose suckers resemble large silvery minnows with blue-green backs.

BUFFALO FISH is a chunky species with a large head; the mouth is located farther forward than in the suckers, and the lips are not as thick and fleshy. The smallmouth buffalo fish is pale silver in color and grows to a length of 36 inches; it lives in the lakes and rivers of the Mississippi River valley. A largemouth buffalo fish is the same size but more olive in color; it is found from Minnesota to Louisiana. Another mem-

The Sucker Family is represented by the creek chub sucker (1), buffalo fish (2), and common sucker (3). Figure 2 adapted from Hubbs and Lagler, "Fishes of the Great Lakes Region," figure 3 from Francesca La Monte, "North American Game Fishes."

ber of the family is the CREEK CHUBSUCKER, widely distributed from New England to the Great Lakes and southward to Texas. Its coloring often includes a pattern of narrow dusky bars. Chubsuckers are usually under 12 inches in length with a deeper body than that of the suckers. The NORTHERN REDHORSE is a pinkish or yellowish fish with red fins; its stout body terminates in a blunt snout that projects beyond the mouth. Large individuals grow to a length of 24 inches and a weight of 10 pounds. This member of the family is found in central United States.

The Live-bearer Family

This family closely resembles the killifishes in many of its features. It is an exclusively American family, with ten species in the United States and many more in Mexico and central America. The best known members are the guppies, aquarium fish native to the tropics. This family (see p. 61) reproduces by internal fertilization of the eggs, which develop within the body of the female. A common species is the MOSQUITO–FISH, which lives in fresh and brackish water of eastern and central United States. It gets its name from its fondness for surface-dwelling larvae such as the "wrigglers" of mosquitoes. This fish is therefore a valuable ally in eliminating malaria through mosquito control. Mosquitofish are silvery in color and only a few inches in length. The females are larger than the males and can be recognized by the enlarged abdominal region. The breeding season is from May to September, each brood numbering up to several hundred young. The newly born mosquitofish are only a third of an inch in length.

The Stickleback Family

Sticklebacks are small spiny-rayed fishes in which the dorsal fin is reduced to separate long spines varying in number from three to nine according to the species. Each ventral fin is also unusual in being reduced to a single spine. About a dozen species occur in both freshwater and marine habitats of north temperate regions; five species occur in the United States. Sticklebacks feed on aquatic plants, crustaceans, and the eggs and fry of fishes. The family is unique in its nest-building activities and in the degree of parental care (see p. 59). The BROOK STICKLEBACK lives in cool streams and small ponds of northern United States from Maine to Montana.

It is a mottled olive-green fish yellowish on the underside and armed with five or six dorsal spines. Full-grown individuals are only a few inches in length, yet the males are ferocious fighters when disturbed, erecting their spines when meeting an adversary. The FOUR-SPINED STICKLEBACK, slightly larger in size, is a species inhabiting brackish estuaries from southern New England to Virginia. The THREE-SPINED STICKLEBACK, found in both brackish waters and lakes of the same range, reaches a length of 4 inches. It is dark green or blue wtih bony plates covering its sides. This species enters fresh waters to spawn.

The Freshwater Eel Family

Although this family includes over a dozen species in Europe and Asia, only one species occurs in the United States. Eels have elongated snakelike bodies covered with small cycloid scales so deeply imbedded in the skin that the eels seem to lack scales entirely. The head of an eel is small and conical; the mouth has true jaws and thereby differs from the somewhat similar lamprey (see p. 206) sometimes mistakenly called an eel. Eels have pectoral fins as well as a low and continuous dorsal fin extending along the back to the tip of the tail. All freshwater eels, as we learned in the story of eel migration, spawn at sea. Landlocked populations of eels occur in the Great Lakes and other inland bodies of fresh water, but eventually these are doomed to die out because eels cannot reproduce in such habitats. Eels were introduced into Lake Michigan in 1877; some still found in their landlocked home sixty years later prove that eels are a very long-lived fish.

The AMERICAN EEL is an olive-brown fish with yellowish sides; when full-grown and ready to return to the sea, the back becomes a darker color and the sides turn silvery. Mature eels are usually 3 to 4 feet in length and weigh up to 5 pounds. They hide among the stones and bottom debris of streams and ponds by day, with only the head visible, and venture forth

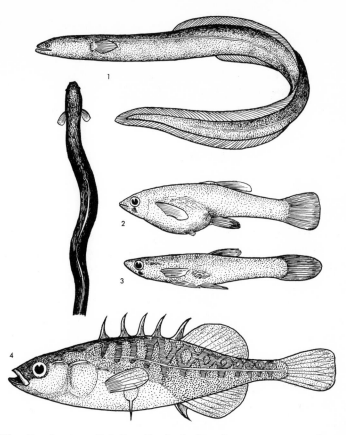

The Freshwater Eel Family includes the common freshwater eel (1). The Live-bearer Family includes the mosquito fish (female, 2 and male, 3) (4). The Stickleback Family includes the brook stickleback. Figures 2, 3, and 4 adapted from Hubbs and Lagler, "Fishes of the Great Lakes Region."

at night to feed. Eels, having small but effective teeth, are voracious carnivores; they are also scavengers, eating any kind of food living or dead. Thus they are often found beneath docks and wharves. Eels mature when 5 to 20 years of age, at such time making their way downstream; the seaward migration begins in summer. In spring a new generation returns to the streams. These elvers, also called glass eels, are only a few inches in length, and transparent and colorless except for a row of black dots along the body. In the upstream passage the mortality rate is high, yet a surprising number of elvers overcome tremendous obstacles to reach their feeding grounds. The survivors join the older eel population, growing in size year by year until they, too, feel the urge to return to the sea.

The Sturgeon Family

Sturgeons are the largest of our freshwater fishes. They are also the most primitive of the bony fishes, in their armored bodies looking like visitors from some prehistoric sea. Of the dozen species found throughout North America and Eurasia, some occur in the sea and others in fresh waters. The center of their abundance is Russia, but seven species occur in the United States. A sturgeon is an elongated fish, flattened on the underside; the body, covered with ganoid scales, is armored in addition with lengthwise rows of bony plates. The single dorsal fin is set far back near the tail fin, which is unsymmetrically forked, the upper lobe being much larger than the lower. The head terminates in a flattened snout bearing a tubular and toothless mouth on the lower surface; in front of the mouth hang four long barbels. These are used to sense the presence of food as the sturgeon cruises along the bottom stirring up the mud. When food is detected the sturgeon extends its mouth and sucks in the prey: worms, crustaceans, and mollusks. The sturgeon feeds as it moves in its sluggish pace; the armored body and rigid fins prevent its starting and stopping quickly. Sturgeon is edible, but its commercial value lies also in the roe, from which caviar is made. A large female lays over two million eggs, which makes fifty pounds of caviar.

The ROCK STURGEON, also known as the lake sturgeon, is the smallest of the American species. It is a light brown or greenish fish with lighter under parts; its average length is 4 feet and its weight about 40 pounds. The rock sturgeon, which inhabits the Great Lakes region, was formerly very abundant in Lake Erie. The ATLANTIC STURGEON, or common sturgeon, as a bluish or olive-green fish that spends most of its life at sea but ascends coastal rivers from New England to the Carolinas to spawn. Prior to 1800 it was very common, but overfishing and stream pollution have greatly reduced its numbers. In former days sturgeons up to 18 feet in length were reportedly caught. Today it is considered a large individual if it reaches a length of 7 feet and a weight of 200 pounds. A sturgeon this size is estimated to be about 12 years old. The female sturgeon lays her eggs in streams, the eggs developing without any parental care. The WHITE STURGEON of the Pacific Coast is the giant of the family, with a maximum length of 12 feet and a weight of over 1000 pounds. It is a greenish gray fish whose body is covered by keeled, or ridge-like plates, each terminating in a spine. The species was formerly very common in the Columbia and Fraser rivers, but the building of dams has prevented this sturgeon from reaching its usual spawning grounds.

The Gar Family

Gars are fishes with elongated cylindrical bodies; both dorsal and anal fins are located far back near the tail. The body is plated with thick diamond-shaped scales of the ganoid type, each scale having an inner core of bone and an outer layer of enamel. The head is prolonged into a beaklike snout with powerful jaws armed with large sharp teeth. Once a numerous group, the gars today are represented by only ten species that quite appropriately can be called living fossils. Five of these species occur in the United States; all live in fresh water, often in stagnant ponds and ditches where few other fishes can survive. Gars are able to breathe without gills by using the air bladder as an emergency lung when they come up to the surface to gulp air. Gars often bask on the surface on warm days, resembling floating logs.

The LONGNOSE GAR, or bony gar, is a widely distrib-

The Sturgeon Family is represented by such huge fishes as the Atlantic sturgeon (1) and lake sturgeon (2). The Gar Family includes the equally large alligator gar (3). Figures 1 and 2 adapted from Hashime Murayama in National Geographic Magazine, 3 from Maynard Reece in Life Magazine.

uted species of sluggish streams and swamps of the central and southern states. Its name is derived from the very long snout, twice as long as the rest of the head. Longnose gars grow to a length of 5 feet; in captivity they have lived to be 20 years old. The ALLIGATOR GAR is the undisputed ruler of the Mississippi River and its tributaries, living in bayous and swampy ponds of southern United States. The name is well given, for when viewed from the front, the fish is startlingly like an alligator because of its huge mouth and numerous dagger-like teeth. This well-armored fish with voracious habits is capable of crushing a 6-foot alligator at a single bite. Like the muskellunge, which it resembles in body build, the alligator gar lies motionless until the prey comes near, then captures it with one quick lunge. In color, the gar is olive-green with silvery sides. A record individual measured 9 feet in length and weighed 300 pounds.

The Bowfin Family

This North American family consists of a single species, and like the gars the bowfin is often called a living fossil. This fish, being able to live several hours out of the water, can survive in the oxygen-deficient stagnant ponds where other fishes die. This is possible because the air bladder functions as a respiratory organ when the bowfin rises to the surface and gulps air. The AMERICAN BOWFIN, also known as mudfish and speckled cat, is an unprepossessing fish inhabiting sluggish streams and swampy ponds from New York to North Dakota southward to the Gulf of Mexico. It is a chunky olive-green fish with yellowish under parts and a covering of large cycloid scales. The blunt head terminates in a large mouth well provided with sharp teeth. The most striking feature, and the one that gives the fish its name, is a long, low dorsal fin that undulates as the fish swims. The paired fins and tail fin are a greenish hue, and during the breeding season an orange-bordered black spot appears at the base of the tail fin of the male. Bowfins grow to a length of 2 or 3 feet and attain a maximum weight of 12 pounds. Hiding among the reeds on a muddy bottom, the bowfin lies in wait for crustaceans and small fishes. Its voracious appetite for the young of game fishes makes this fish most unpopular with fishermen. During spawning, the male clears a circular area among the grasses as a nest where the female deposits the eggs; the latter hatch in one week, but the young remain near the nest for several weeks more, guarded by the male. Even after they leave the nest, the young bowfins are protected by the male who carefully herds them in a group while feeding.

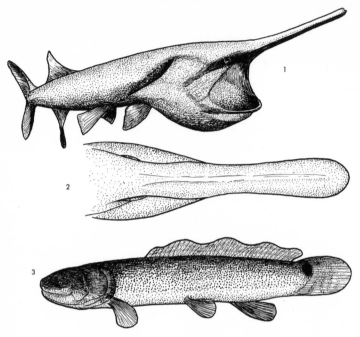

Two unique fishes found in fresh water are the paddlefish (1), with view of duck-like bill from above (2), and the bowfin (3). Figure 1 adapted from Walter Chute, "Guide to the Shedd Aquarium"; 3 from Hubbs and Lagler, "Fishes of the Great Lakes Region."

The Paddlefish Family

Only two species make up this family, one found in China and the other in the United States. The grotesque paddlefishes have many primitive traits, among them a skeleton of cartilage. The most unusual feature is the long paddlelike snout that makes up about one-third of the body length. This is a flexible structure with a bony base, extremely sensitive and easily injured. Such an appendage is undoubtedly more of a handicap than of any special advantage. The single soft-rayed dorsal fin is located far back near the deeply forked tail fin. The AMERICAN PADDLEFISH, also known as spoon-bill cat and shovelnose cat, lives in silty lakes and ponds of central and southern United States. It is a grayish fish that grows to a length of 6 feet and may weigh as much as 150 pounds. It is a filter-feeder, maintaining its huge bulk on a diet of plankton that is strained from the water by the sievelike gill rakers in the throat. Little is known of the spawning habits and early life history of this strange member of our freshwater community.

*Members of the Jack Family are sleek saltwater game fishes
with a hard keel on each side of the narrow tail.*

Chapter Five

Saltwater Game Fishes

The United States is fortunate in having thousands of miles of shoreline bordering on two major oceans, with habitats that range from the cold waters of the Gulf of Maine and Puget Sound to the subtropical wonderlands of the Florida Keys and Catalina Island. In these waters live an even greater abundance and variety of fishes than those we have just met in our streams and lakes. The shallow inshore waters teem with many fishes familiar to the fisherman of piers, bridges, and channel banks. Offshore are many other kinds of game fishes accessible to those who have any kind of craft from an outboard skiff to a luxurious fishing cruiser. There are over a hundred common species of saltwater game fishes, some of which we will now meet. The identification of these can be simplified by grouping the fishes into a few categories on the basis of features that they have in common. The most useful of these are the type of dorsal fin, the size of the scales, the feeding habits, and the body proportions. Using these, we can distinguish four large groups of saltwater game fishes.

Group 1. The greatest number of families have a single dorsal fin with a spiny forward portion and a soft-rayed posterior portion. Elongated bodies, about three times as long as deep, are typical of the *Sea Bass Family,* the *Drum Family,* the *Snapper Family,* and the *Wrasse Family.* More chunky bodies, only twice as long as deep, are found in the *Porgy Family.* These families are made up of species that are, for the most part, inhabitants of the Atlantic coastal waters. Two other families are found only off the Pacific Coast: the *Greenling Family* and the *Surfperch Family.*

Group 2. Another smaller group of families is characterized by two dorsal fins, the forward spiny dorsal being more or less separate from the soft-rayed dorsal fin. In the *Bluefish Family* the two dorsal fins are very close together, and the body is long and slender, about four times as long as deep. The *Mullet Family* also includes fishes with elongated bodies of the same proportions. Largest and most important of this group is the *Mackerel Family,* which has such well-known members as the tunas. They are marvelously streamlined fishes noted for their speed; they possess a distinctive series of small finlets aft of both the dorsal and anal fins. Most slender and streamlined of all are the members of the *Barra- cuda Family,* with bodies often five or six times as long as deep. The *Jack Family* is a group of more chunky fishes, two or three times as long as deep, with a prominent keel on either side of the tail.

Group 3. A few families can be recognized by their single dorsal fin that lacks any separation into a spiny and a soft- rayed portion. Three well-known game fishes belong to this group. The *Tarpon Family* features a small dorsal fin and a body covering of extremely large scales. The *Bonefish Family* also has a relatively small dorsal fin but smaller scales. In the *Dolphin Family* the head is blunt and a long, high dorsal fin extends the entire length of the back.

Group 4. Here can be placed two unusual families that can be recognized by an elongated upper jaw that extends forward as a flattened sword or a cylindrical spear. Such a formidable weapon is borne by members of the *Billfish Family,* whose best-known members are the marlins and sailfishes. It is also characteristic of the *Swordfish Family.*

Table 6. Rod-and-Reel Saltwater World Records

Species	Weight (in pounds and ounces)	Length (in feet and inches)	Where Caught
Amberjack	120– 8	5– 2	Hawaii
Barracuda	103– 4	5– 6	Bahama Islands
Bass, Cal. Black	514	7– 2	California
Bass, Channel	83	4– 4	Virginia
Bass, Giant Sea	551	8– 4	Texas
Bass, Striped	73– 5	5	Massachusetts
Bluefish	24– 3	3– 5	Azores
Bonefish	18– 2	3– 5	Hawaii
Bonito	39–15	3– 3	Bahamas
Cod	74– 4	5– 6	Maine
Dolphin	76	5– 3	Mexico
Drum, Black	94– 4	4– 3	Virginia
Marlin, Black	1,560	14– 6	Peru
Marlin, Striped	692	13– 5	California
Marlin, White	161	8– 8	Florida
Permit	47–12	3– 9	Florida
Pollock	42	4– 4	Massachusetts
Sailfish, Pacific	221	10– 9	Galapagos Islands
Swordfish	1,182	14–11	Chile
Tarpon	283	7– 2	Venezuela
Tuna, Bluefin	977	9– 8	Nova Scotia
Weakfish	17– 8	3–10	New Jersey

The Sea Bass Family

The *Sea Bass Family* is a large one, with sixty species in the United States, some found off the Atlantic Coast and others off the Pacific. In Chapter Three (see p. 90) we described the freshwater members of the family, white bass and yellow bass. Marine species include a number of kinds of sea bass and in addition the warm-water fishes known as groupers.

STRIPED BASS, also known as rockfish and greenhead, is a brassy pink or brownish fish with dark green head and back and a silvery belly; lengthwise stripes occur along the sides. The ventral fins are set far forward beneath the pectoral fins, as in other members of the family. Average individuals weigh up to 10 pounds; a record size is 125 pounds, the weight of a 6 foot specimen. Native to the Atlantic Coast from New England to Florida, striped bass is most common from Cape Cod to the Carolinas. It is one of the few marine game fishes that have been successfully introduced on the Pacific Coast. This bass is found near shore where it feeds on smaller fishes, crustaceans, and worms; it is a favorite with surf fishermen and is also a commercially important food fish. Striped bass spawn in river mouths, being especially abundant during the spawning season in Chesapeake Bay. The eggs develop as they drift in the water, hatching in 2 or 3 days.

BLACK SEA BASS, also known as blackfish or common sea bass, is a more sluggish bottom-feeding species found along the Atlantic Coast from Cape Cod to Virginia. It is a dark brown fish with a bluish gray back; the rounded tail fin has a prolonged ray at its upper tip, and the pectoral fins are wide and rounded. An average black bass is under 18 inches in length and less than 3 pounds in weight, but some individuals grow to a length of 24 inches and weigh 8 pounds. The male differs from the female in having longer fin rays and a fatty hump in front of the dorsal fin. Black sea bass remain offshore in winter but in summer enter the bays and inlets where they often are found in the shadows beneath wharves and about submerged wrecks. Black sea bass is a commercial food fish of the mid-Atlantic Coast and is also a common species caught by fishing party boats.

A few members of the family are game fishes of the Pacific coastal waters. The CALIFORNIA KELP BASS, or cabrilla, is an olive-gray fish with pinkish belly and green fins; an average individual measures about 20 inches and weighs under 5 pounds. Kelp bass are caught for the most part in winter as they feed on small organisms living in the kelp beds. This species is most common south of San Francisco. The

GIANT SEA BASS, or California black bass, is the largest member of the family on the Pacific Coast; it is most abundant south of San Diego. This is a dusky brown or black bass whose stout dorsal spines can be lowered into a groove along the back. It is a huge fish, few individuals being caught that weigh less than 50 pounds, and some weigh as much as 500 pounds. Giant sea bass live on rocky bottoms where they feed on crustaceans and small fishes living in such habitats.

Groupers are stout, often clumsy-looking fishes whose bodies are covered by small ctenoid scales deeply embedded in the skin. Other characteristics of these members of the sea bass family are the large mouth, ventral fins set far forward beneath the pectorals, strong spines on the gill cover, and the rounded margin on the tail fin. Groupers get their name as a result of their habit of hovering in small groups. As might be expected from their body proportions, they swim slowly and feed upon small fishes and slow-moving crustaceans. Over a hundred species occur in all the warm seas, many being commercially important as food fishes. Groupers have two interesting habits. They are the chameleons of the fish world, capable of rapid and varied color changes. They also are always hungry and are so unafraid of man that they can be tempted to take food from the hands of divers.

The NASSAU GROUPER, or rockfish, is a West Indian species that is found northward to the Florida coast. It has numerous color phases and can change from one to the other rapidly, usually matching the color to that of the environment. Sometimes it is gray with vertical brown bars; at other times it is white, tan, or brown and may be mottled or blotched in a blending of these colors. The Nassau grouper is a large fish, 2 to 3 feet in length and weighing up to 50 pounds. It is both a game fish and a food fish; it is caught most frequently by anglers off the Florida keys. The RED GROUPER, or red-bellied snapper, is a more northern species found as far up the Atlantic Coast as Virginia. Its usual color is a warm mottled brown, but its color ranges from a reddish

The Bluefish Family has a single member, the Atlantic blue-fish (1). The Sea Bass Family includes black sea bass (2), striped bass (3), jewfish (4), black grouper (5) and giant black California bass (6). Figures 1, 2, 3, 5 adapted from Hashime Murayama in National Geographic Magazine; 4 from Marineland (Florida) photo; 6 from Maynard Reece in Life Magazine.

tan to a solid black. Red groupers are smaller than the Nassau, being about 24 inches in length and weighing under 25 pounds. They are bottom-feeders, hiding among submarine caverns and hollows where they feed on shrimp, other crustaceans, and octopus. The BLACK GROUPER, also known as the Warsaw grouper, is a common fish off the Florida gulf coast. It, too, has changeable color but usually is a dusky reddish gray with horizontal black markings. The black grouper is usually under 3 feet in length and weighs less than 10 pounds, although extremely large ones sometimes weigh as much as 50 pounds. This species prefers to stay on offshore banks and reefs where it feeds on mullets and other small fishes. Giant of the sea bass family is the huge JEW-FISH, known also as the black grouper, a tropical fish ranging northward into Florida waters. This clumsy but harmless giant is mottled black in color and has a very large head. An average individual weighs about 50 pounds, but large specimens may reach a length of 6 feet and weigh as much as 600 pounds. Jewfish lives along rocky shores and under wharves, feeding on smaller fishes. Although not a game fish, its large size often attracts fishermen and scuba divers.

The Drum Family

This is another large family of food and game fishes living in temperate and warm seas; it includes over thirty species in the United States. One—the freshwater drum—makes its home in rivers and lakes. The dorsal fin of a drum often consists of a soft-rayed portion that is much longer than the forward spiny part. The tail fin has a squarecut or rounded margin. Members of this family make a variety of drumming and croaking noises that can be heard for some distance above the water (see p. 49). Some members of the group have barbels on the lower jaw: croakers, black drum, and the kingfishes. Others lack the barbels as in red drum and silver bass.

BLACK DRUM, or sea drum, is a favorite among beach

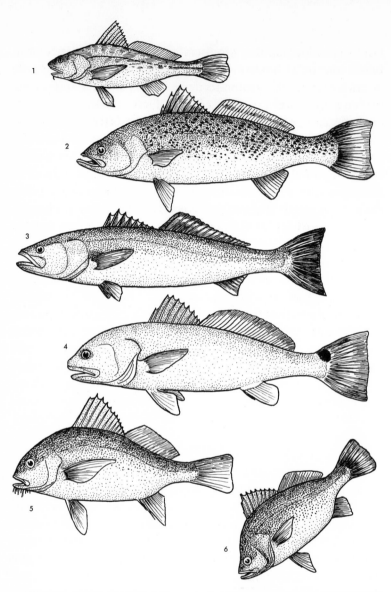

The large Drum Family includes northern kingfish (1), weak-fish (2), white sea bass (3), red drum (4), black drum (5), and silver perch (6). Figures 1, 2, 5, 6 adapted from Francesca La Monte, "North American Game Fishes"; 3 and 4 from Maynard Reece in Life Magazine.

fishermen who surfcast along the Atlantic Coast. In oyster-producing bays, however, it is considered a menace because of its forays in the mollusks beds. Black drum is a bottom-feeder, crushing the mollusks upon which it subsists by means of the grinding pharyngeal teeth in the throat. This drum is a dusky gray to coppery black fish with a stout, deep body and a cluster of barbels beneath the chin; the spiny dorsal fin is much higher than the soft-rayed dorsal. The black drum is usually under 6 pounds in weight, but a large 4-foot black drum may weigh over 40 pounds. With its scraggly "beard" and humped back, it is hardly a beautiful fish. Black drums appear in schools off beaches and in bays from New York to Texas. They are particularly noisy during the breeding season, both sexes being able to produce the drumming sounds.

RED DRUM, also known as channel bass and red bass, is a metallic bronze or pinkish fish with faint lengthwise brown stripes and a black spot at the base of the tail fin. This drum turns a bright red after it is caught. A large individual grows to a length of 5 feet and weighs up to 75 pounds. It differs from the black drum, in addition to its coloring, by lacking the chin barbels found in the former species. Red drum occurs along sandy shores from New Jersey to Texas, where it is a surfcaster's favorite fish.

The FRESHWATER DRUM, or freshwater sheepshead, is a species of silty lakes and large rivers where it feeds along the bottom in the muddy water on snails and mussels, crushed by the powerful pharyngeal teeth. It occurs from the Great Lakes southward through central United States. This drum is a metallic blue-green fish with yellowish tints; the average size is 15 inches in length and 2 pounds in weight. In Lake Erie, where it is common, this species is a commercial food fish. A revealing aspect of the give-and-take that occurs in nature is the fact that, as the drum feeds on mussels, it becomes infected with the young swimming mussels known as glochidia. When the drum moves into new feeding grounds, the glochidia are eventually released and form new mussel beds. Thus the fish effectively if unconsciously assists in maintaining an ample supply of its favorite food.

Several kinds of drums are popularly known as croakers because of their vocal efforts. The ATLANTIC CROAKER, otherwise known as hardhead or corvina, is a silvery green or grayish fish with lighter sides marked by a pattern of indistinct wavy bars. The dorsal fin is deeply notched between the spiny and the soft-rayed portions; the mouth is on the underside of the head and the lower jaw bears a row of minute barbels. A croaker is usually under 12 inches in length and weighs about 1 pound, although occasionally fish weighing 4 pounds are caught. Like other members of the family it is a bottom-feeder on mollusks and crustaceans. In summer it frequents sandy shores from New Jersey to Texas but in winter moves out to sea. In the Chesapeake Bay region this species is an important food fish as well as a game fish. Some croaker species occur on the Pacific Coast. The YELLOW-FIN CROAKER, or roncador, is a metallic-looking fish with dark back and sides marked by lengthwise stripes; the belly is rosy, and the fins are yellow. It grows to a length of 12 inches. The yellowfin croaker is a fish of sandy shores, especially abundant off the coast of southern California. The SPOTFIN CROAKER is a larger fish, weighing up to 5 pounds, found in the surf of sandy beaches of California north to San Francisco. This is a bluish species with brassy sides and dusky fins; each pectoral fin has a black spot at its base.

The WHITE SEA BASS is another Pacific Coast member of the family, abundant from Santa Barbara southward along the California coast. This relative of the croakers is an elongated metallic blue fish with silvery sides; the chin lacks barbels and the pectoral fins are unusually long and narrow. This is a large species, attaining a weight of 80 pounds. It is a favorite inshore game fish as well as a food fish of some importance. The best fishing for white sea bass is from April to September near islands or kelp beds where the bass feed on their chief diet of crab, shrimp, and herring.

SILVER PERCH, or sand perch, a greenish or bluish-gray fish with silvery sides, is found from New York to Texas; the chin lacks barbels, and the front of the gill cover is edged with spines. Although the silver perch grows to a length of 12 inches, young fishes about 6 inches in length make up the average catch along the mid-Atlantic Coast. This member of the drum family is sometimes confused with the white perch but differs in having two anal fins instead of three and in having the lateral line extend into the tail fin. Silver perch, like many other shore fishes, lays buoyant eggs that hatch as they float; the hatching time is a remarkably short one, taking only two days.

WEAKFISH, which is known also as sea trout and sque-teague, is a favorite dinner fish of the mid-Atlantic states. It occurs from New England to Florida, being caught only in the summer in the northern part of its range but the year round in the south. In this member of the drum family, the spiny portion of the dorsal fin is higher than the soft-rayed portion and slightly separated from it. Weakfish is greenish blue and silvery, with the upper sides marked by a pattern of oblique wavy bars of brown or green. The lower jaw projects beyond the upper, which has two prominent front teeth. The average individual is 30 inches in length and weighs 5 pounds. Its name refers to the tender mouth that is torn easily by a hook. Weakfish feed on smaller fishes found in surf and swiftly flowing channels. Like other members of the family, it is valuable both as a food fish and as a game fish.

NORTHERN KINGFISH, or whiting, is an elongated fish with a gray and silver coloring, marked by irregular oblique bars on the upper sides; the spiny dorsal fin is higher than the soft-rayed dorsal. A conspicuous barbel hangs from the chin and the tail fin has an S-shaped margin. This kingfish is of moderate size, usually 12 to 17 inches in length and weighing about 3 pounds. It is unusual in having no air bladder and in being very sensitive to weather changes. Northern kingfish withdraws to offshore waters at the approach of a cold spell, reappearing near shore again when the weather is warm. This species occurs along the Atlantic Coast from New York to Maryland, where it is a common surfcaster's fish. The SOUTHERN KINGFISH is a silvery gray and white also but lacks the prolonged dorsal spines of its northern relative. This species, of the same size as the northern whiting, is most common south of Chesapeake Bay. On the Pacific Coast the CALIFORNIA KINGFISH, or white croaker, is found from San Francisco southward. It is a small silvery brown fish with yellowsh fins and oblique wavy markings on the upper sides.

The Snapper Family

The snappers, another large family of warm-water fishes, are represented by sixteen species off the Atlantic Coast. They are basslike fishes with an oblong body, a large mouth provided with unequally sized teeth, and a slightly forked tail fin. Unlike the groupers, snappers usually congregate in schools. They have a reputation for craftiness, taking the bait with a quick darting movement that requires an alert fisherman to make a catch.

The RED SNAPPER is a deep red or brick-colored fish with an average length of 2 feet and a weight of less than 25 pounds. It is abundant in the Gulf of Mexico, although individuals sometimes wander up the Atlantic Coast as far north as New York. Red snappers are an important food fish, with the center for the commercial catch in Florida. The GRAY SNAPPER, or mangrove snapper, is a smaller fish of changeable coloring, sometimes being gray or brown and at other times a brassy green with reddish gray sides. It is a bottom-feeder common from Florida to Texas. The VERMILION SNAPPER or rockfish is a brilliantly colored species with red and yellow hues; it is usually 12 inches in length and under 3 pounds in weight. Vermilion snappers are also bottom-feeders found from the Carolinas to the Gulf of Mexico. MUTTONFISH, also known as mutton snapper, is a large member of the family growing to a length of 27 inches and weighing up to 25 pounds. It is a very colorful species with an olive-tinted back, light red sides, rose red belly, brick red paired fins, and a yellow dorsal fin. Little wonder that this snapper, common on the Florida reefs, locally is called the reef king.

The Porgy Family

This is a small family of fishes with large heads and high backs; of the fifteen species found in the United States all but one is confined to the Atlantic Coast. As in many families of marine fishes, the eggs are buoyant and float near the surface; they hatch in the record-breaking time of forty hours.

The NORTHERN SCUP, or common porgy, is a brownish fish with silvery belly and dusky fins; the spiny portion of the dorsal fin is much higher and longer than the soft-rayed portion. The eyes are set high on the sloping head, which terminates in a small snout. Northern scup grows to a length of 18 inches and a maximum weight of 4 pounds. They appear in tremendous schools during summer in inshore waters from Maine to the Carolinas; in winter the schools move out to sea into deeper and warmer water. Porgies are bottom-feeders subsisting on a diet of crustaceans, mollusks, worms, and small fishes. This species is more of a commercial food fish than a game fish throughout most of its range. The GRASS PORGY is a more colorful southern species living amid the eelgrass off the Florida coast. It is a smaller, olive-hued fish with dark bars and spots, spotted fins, and yellow spots along the lateral line. SHEEPSHEAD, the best known game fish of the family, is an Atlantic Coast species ranging from Cape Cod to Florida. It resembles the northern scup in shape but has a more distinctive appearance because of seven wide black vertical

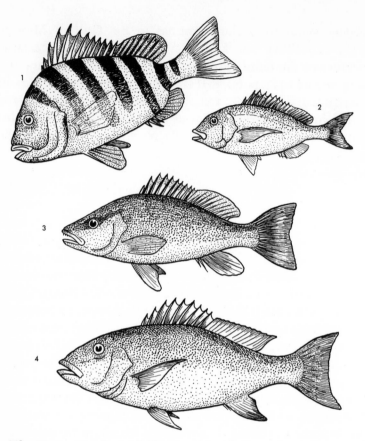

The Porgy Family includes sheepshead (1) and northern scup or porgy (2). The Snapper Family includes gray snapper (3) and muttonfish (4). All figures adapted from Maynard Reece in Life Magazine.

stripes that extend from the back to the belly; the background coloring is olive-green. The name sheepshead refers to the sudden rise of the forward end of the body to a hump above the eyes. Average individuals are 24 to 30 inches long and weigh up to 6 pounds, although 20-pound fishes are sometimes caught. Sheepshead, being a bottom-feeder on mussels and barnacles, is frequently found beneath piers and among the timbers of submerged wrecks.

The Wrasse Family

This is a family of predominantly warm-water fishes, with over twenty species in the United States, all but three of which are found on the Atlantic Coast only. They have oblong bodies covered with cycloid scales, and the mouth is provided with strong jaw teeth as well as powerful pharyngeal teeth used in crushing mollusks. Many brilliantly colored species are inhabitants of coral reefs. Familiar northern members of the family are cunner and tautog; hogfish and California sheepshead are southern and western specis. Only a few species of the family are considered game fishes.

The CUNNER, found from New England to New Jersey, is an omnivorous fish that feeds on seaweeds and small marine invertebrates; it is the most northern member of the family, living on rocky bottoms and haunting the water beneath piers and docks. Cunners range in color from a dark olive-green to a reddish green or brown depending upon the color of the surroundings. A common member of the inshore fish population, the cunner—although unexciting to catch—is frequently caught for use as a pan fish. Large individuals reach a length of 15 inches and weigh several pounds. The TAUTOG, or blackfish, is a large unprepossessing fish mottled brown in coloring. It grows to a length of 36 inches and may weigh as much as 20 pounds. It differs from a cunner by having a blunter snout. The jaws are armed with two rows of teeth, and additional pharyngeal teeth aid in crushing mollusks. Tautogs range from Cape Cod south to the Delaware River, being found inshore during the summer and in winter offshore in deeper water. Fishermen consider the tautog a nuisance since it bites readily and is difficult to unhook, yet is not a particularly good game or food fish.

On the Pacific Coast is found the CALIFORNIA SHEEPS-HEAD, also called fathead and California redfish. This is a conspicuously marked fish, with a black or dusky body crossed vertically by a broad saddle of bright red. The dorsal spiny fin and the pectoral fins also are red. In profile this fish has a very high "forehead"; in the breeding season the head of the male is elevated even more by the development of a fatty hump. This species weighs on the average about 15 pounds. HOGFISH is a tropical member of the reef fishes living around Key West, Florida. It is a reddish brown or gray fish with projecting front teeth and very ornate fins. The first three dorsal spines form long streamers, and the anal fin and posterior dorsal fin extend into tapering tips. Hogfish reaches a weight of 12 to 15 pounds.

The Greenling Family

This small family, with seven American species, is found only on the Pacific Coast. It is a cold-water group of fishes of which the lingcod and kelp greenling are common representatives. They have a large mouth, protruding lower jaw, and sharp teeth both in the jaws and in the roof of the mouth. LINGCOD, found from California to Alaska, is a mottled brown or gray fish often spotted with blue or red. The long dorsal fin has a deep notch between the spiny and the soft-rayed portions; the tail fin is square-cut, and the pectoral fins are unusually broad. In this species the female is much larger than the male, weighing as much as 70 pounds while the male rarely weighs more than 30. Lingcod is chiefly a food fish of some commercial value. KELP GREENLING is a smaller fish about 18 inches in length; it is grayish brown or coppery, variously spotted and blotched. Like the lingcod it has a deep notch between the two portions of the dorsal fin. As the name indicates, it is commonly caught near kelp beds; the range is the same as that of lingcod.

The Surfperch Family

This is another small Pacific Coast family. As the common name suggests, these fishes live in the surf zone along sandy

The Surfperch Family includes striped perch (1). The Wrasse Family includes cunner (2), hogfish (3), California sheepshead (4), and tautog (5). The Greenling Family includes lingcod (6). All figures adapted from Francesca La Monte, "North American Game Fishes."

shores. Surfperches have short deep bodies and one continuous long dorsal fin. The family is one of the few marine bony fishes that give birth to living young. Many of the species, though small, are considered good game fishes. The BARRED SURFPERCH, found from California to Washington, is a metallic blue fish with rosy belly and a pattern of indistinct vertical bars on the sides. It is usually under 8 inches in length. The STRIPED PERCH, or blue sea perch, has the same range. This surfperch is a colorful fish with dusky back, olive-green fins, and numerous lengthwise stripes of blue and red. Its length is the same as that of the barred surfperch, although occasionally a 15-inch fish is landed. Striped perch lurk around piers and docks feeding on shrimps, worms, and other small aquatic animals.

The Bluefish Family

This family has the internal structure of the sea bass family but resembles the mackerel family in external features. The ATLANTIC BLUEFISH is the only species in the family. It is a streamlined greenish blue fish with silvery sides. The spiny dorsal fin is much smaller than the long soft-rayed portion, and the division between the two is very slight. The ventral fins are set far forward beneath the pectorals as in perch and bass; the tail is deeply forked as in all fast-swimming fishes. The large powerful jaws, armed with sharp teeth, reveal the carnivorous habits of the bluefish, which is often called the wolf of the sea because of killing much more prey than it can eat. It has been estimated that one bluefish in the midst of a school of mackerel or menhaden can kill a thousand fish a day. The average bluefish is under 24 inches in length and less than 2 pounds in weight; a large individual may be 48 inches long and weigh 25 pounds. Bluefish are widely distributed in the Atlantic Ocean from Florida to New England; they are a favorite food-and-game fish of the mid-Atlantic states. Young bluefish, known as snappers, enter coastal waters in spring and remain throughout the summer; they are caught by surfcasters and by still fishermen on piers and bridges. In spite of their abundance and importance, little is known of their spawning and breeding habits.

The Mackerel Family

The *Mackerel Family* is an important one, with sixty widespread species ranging the high seas all over the world in both temperate and tropical waters. In the family are many valuable food fishes as well as prized game fishes. About one third of the species is found in American waters, some on the Pacific Coast and some on the Atlantic. Members of the family are typically cigar-shaped fishes built for speed. The body is covered with minute cycloid scales, and the forward end tapers to a large mouth armed with sharp teeth. The fins of some species can fold and fit snugly into grooves, thus being out of the way when the fish is swimming. An unusual feature is the presence of small finlets between the tail fin, and the dorsal and the anal fins. The tail, except in the common mackerel, has keels along each side and terminates in a deeply forked tail fin. Most of the species are rovers traveling over vast stretches of the ocean in pursuit of schools of smaller fishes. The family includes several kinds of mackerel, tuna, albacore, and wahoo.

ATLANTIC MACKEREL, also known as Boston mackerel or northern mackerel, is a blue-green fish with silvery sides marked by irregular dark bars. It is usually about 12 inches in length and weighs 1 pound; large individuals may be 20 inches and weigh as much as 4 pounds. Atlantic mackerel is a cold-water fish found from Labrador to the mid-Atlantic states. Schools of mackerel approach the shore in spring, move out to deeper water in winter. Small mackerel, 10 inches or less in size and known as tinker mackerel, appear suddenly in great numbers in bays and mouths of rivers. Mackerel sometimes congregate in schools of incredible proportions, as much as 20 miles in length and ½ mile in width. Mackerel eggs are buoyant, hatching in five days as they drift. Eggs and young, as well as adults, are the prey of larger carnivores such as bluefish and shark; the species is so prolific, however, that their numbers remain constant.

SPANISH MACKEREL, or southern mackerel, lives in the warmer waters of the Atlantic from the Carolinas to Florida.

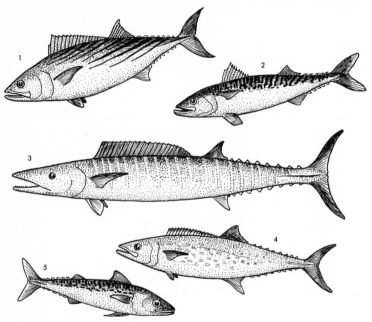

The Mackerel Family includes bonito (1), Atlantic mackerel (2), wahoo (3), Spanish mackerel (4), and Pacific mackerel (5). Figures 1, 3, 4 adapted from Maynard Reece in Life Magazine; 2 and 5 from Hasime Murayama in National Geographic Magazine.

It differs from the northern species in having a keel on each side of the tail. The dark blue back and silvery sides are sometimes marked by orange or red spots. The long low spiny portion and the higher soft-rayed portion of the almost continuous dorsal fin are also distinctive features. The average weight is 2 pounds, but specimens 6 feet in length have been caught that weigh 20 pounds. Spanish mackerel is also an oceanic wanderer but at times forms large schools near shore. As a game fish it strikes hard, fights stubbornly, and jumps out of the water as spectacularly as a dolphin. The PACIFIC MACKEREL, found from California to Alaska, is a metallic green fish with silvery sides whose upper portion is marked by oblique bars. It is a small fish, 12 inches in length and weighing under 2 pounds. Sport fishermen enjoy its fighting qualities, but because of its small size, it is not a popular game fish.

The ATLANTIC BONITO, also known as horse mackerel or little tunny, is a marvel of compact strength and beauty; its torpedo-shaped body and smoothly polished surface reduce water resistance to a minimum and place the bonito among the champion ocean swimmers. It has the coloring of a mackerel, but the upper sides are marked by numerous oblique dark-blue bars extending upward and backward from the lateral line. The sharply pointed finlets give the tail a saw-toothed appearance, and the long spiny dorsal fin is almost continuous with the soft-rayed portion of the fin. Although the average size is under 24 inches and 5 pounds, larger individuals up to 30 inches and 15 pounds are sometimes hooked. It gathers in schools near the surface as far north as Cape Cod, and preys on mackerel and menhaden. Atlantic bonito can often be seen leaping out of the water as it pursues its prey.

Two of the smaller tunas are the albacore and the little tuna. The ALBACORE, or long-finned tuna, like other tunas has a long spiny dorsal fin that is almost continuous with the posterior soft-rayed portion. It differs in the extremely long and tapering pectoral fins that may be half the length of the body; small, smooth scales contribute a sleek surface to this fast swimmer, and added speed comes from the deeply forked and crescent-shaped tail fin. All the fins fit into grooves, another adaptation for swift locomotion through the water. Albacore has a dark blue head and back and silvery yellow

sides. It is primarily a warm-water fish found off the Florida
and California shores, although it ranges north to Cape Cod
and Puget Sound. An albacore is usually less than 36 inches
in length and under 30 pounds in weight. Its vigorous fight
when hooked makes it a good game fish, but it is also an important food fish in the tuna canning industry. The LITTLE
TUNA, or false albacore, is a bluish green fish with distinctive
oblique wavy lines on the upper sides and spots behind the
pectoral fins. It is 24 inches or less in length and weighs 5
pounds or under. False albacore roams the entire Atlantic
Coast in large schools; during summer it is commonly caught
by sport fishermen trolling offshore in the vicinity of New
York City.

The YELLOWFIN TUNA is a warm-water species found
on the Atlantic Coast south of Maryland and on the southern
Pacific Coast. It is a dark blue fish with silvery sides, and
yellow fins and often with a yellow stripe from eye to tail;
these brilliant colors fade soon after the fish is caught. Large
individuals are 6 feet in length and weigh as much as 200
pounds. In old individuals the dorsal and anal fins are extremely elongated. This is commercially the most valuable
tuna. The annual catch runs into hundreds of millions of
pounds with a value of over thirty million dollars. Specially
equipped fishing boats of the tuna fleets can haul in, by hook
and line, hundreds of yellowfins in a day.

BLUEFIN TUNA, known as tunny in Europe, is not only
the largest member of the mackerel family but is also one of
the largest living fishes. This "tiger of the sea" grows to a
length of 14 feet and weighs as much as 1500 pounds; the
average bluefin, however, weighs under 200 pounds. Bluefin
tuna is an iridescent fish with steely blue head and back,
silvery sides, and often with a yellowish or purple stripe
separating the blue and the silver. The dusky fins may be
tinged with yellow, and the small finlets are bright yellow.
The soft-rayed dorsal and anal fins are long and taper to a
point. In addition to its importance as a food fish, this tuna is

considered one of the gamest sport fishes of the sea. It is a wide-ranging species found on both shores of the Atlantic as well as in the Pacific and Indian oceans. Famous fishing grounds on the Atlantic Coast are located in Casco Bay,

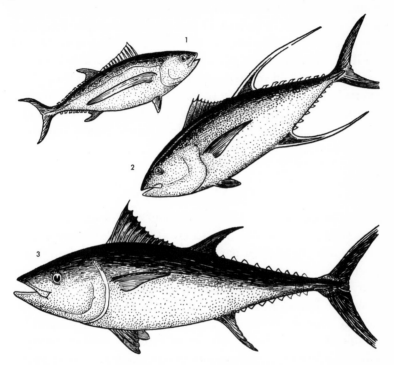

Important food and game fishes in the Mackerel Family include albacore (1), yellowfin tuna (2) and bluefin tuna (3). Figure 1 adapted from Francesca La Monte, "North American Game Fishes"; figure 2 from Hashime Murayama in National Geographic Magazine; figure 3 from Maynard Reece in Life Magazine.

Maine; off Ipswich, Massachusetts; and off Montauk, New York. On the Pacific Coast the bluefin occurs from California to Oregon, with good fishing grounds off Catalina Island. A bluefin on the hook has been described as a living meteor that strikes like a whirlwind and plays like a storm. This huge carnivore requires great quantities of food and, as a result, consumes thousands of herring and mackerel. In turn, the bluefin is preyed upon by its arch enemy, the killer whale.

The WAHOO is a slender and elongated member of the mackerel family, looking more like a pike or a barracuda than a tuna; in fact another common name for this species is ocean barracuda. The wahoo is a sleek fish with a long, low spiny dorsal fin and a smaller soft-rayed fin. The steel blue of the dorsal fins and back blends into silvery blue sides that are sometimes marked indistinctly by vertical gray or yellow bars. Average individuals are 15 to 30 pounds in weight. This fast-swimming carnivore is a solitary hunter preying on smaller fishes. It occurs in warm Atlantic waters, being especially abundant about the Florida Keys.

The Mullet Family

This small family of six American species occurs for the most part along the Atlantic Coast. The mullet is not strictly a game fish but is often part of the catch of a sport fisherman; its greatest importance is as a commercial food fish. The small spiny dorsal fin is set far forward from the equally small soft-rayed fin. The elongated body terminates in a small head and mouth. Because of the abundance of fat in the broad rounded back, some mullets are known as fatbacks. Mullets have a habit of playfully jumping out of the water for no apparent reason. The STRIPED MULLET is a bluish or greenish gray fish with a pattern of faint horizontal stripes on its sides. On the Atlantic Coast striped mullet is not common north of New York. Individuals range from 12 to 24 inches in length. The body is covered with large scales somewhat similar to those of tarpon. Striped mullet also is found south of Monterey on the California coast. Mullets feed on small organisms that they dig out of the muddy bottom. WHITE MULLET, a more tropical species, grows to a length of 36 inches. Its back is dark green and the light silvery sides are unstriped. This species is abundant in the Gulf of Mexico.

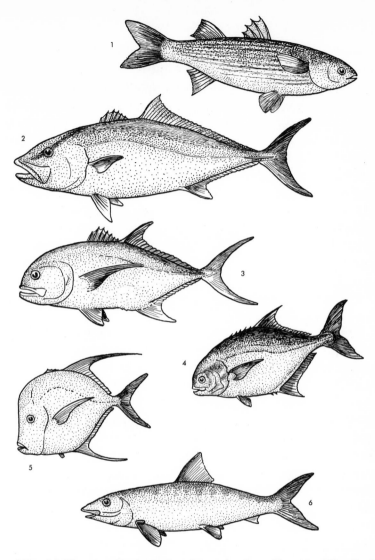

The Mullet Family includes the striped mullet (1). The Jack Family includes amberjack (2), jack crevalle (3), pompano(4) and lookdown (5). The Bonefish Family includes the common bonefish (6). Figure 1 adapted from Hashime Murayama in National Geographic Magazine; 2, 3, 6 from Maynard Reece in Life Magazine; 4 from Francesca La Monte, "North American Game Fishes."

The Jack Family

This is a large family of warm-water fishes represented in the United States by over thirty species found off both the Atlantic and Pacific coasts. Most members of the family have two separate dorsal fins, although in some species the spiny dorsal is close to the soft-rayed portion and in other species it is reduced to small separate spines. The posterior dorsal and anal fins are low and long, often reaching to the tail fin. Some species have a unique keel along the posterior part of the lateral line, strengthening the narrow tail. The family includes many popular game and food fishes: amberjack, crevalle jack, rudderfish, runner, lookdown, pompano, and permit.

The GREATER AMBERJACK or yellowtail, a common fish of Florida waters, occasionally wanders as far north as Cape Cod. It is a delicately tinted fish with silvery lavender sides and a dusky back, and its body is covered with very small scales. The spiny dorsal is much smaller than the tapering soft-rayed fin, which extends back to the tail. The name comes from the fact this fish turns an amber color after it is caught. Amberjacks feed on shrimp, squid, and smaller fishes. An average amberjack weighs about 15 pounds, but individuals up to 100 pounds are often caught. A PACIFIC AMBER-JACK is a somewhat larger blue and silver fish with a conspicuous yellow stripe extending from eye to tail. It is found south of San Diego during the summer months. The CRE-VALLE JACK is a smaller fish usually weighing less than 10 pounds and with a more compact body than the amberjack and a high sloping forehead; the pectoral fins are long and gracefully tapering. It is a golden yellow fish with lavender tints to the silvery sides. This jack occurs in schools along the Atlantic Coast north to Cape Cod. The BLUE RUNNER, or hardtail jack, is similar in appearance to the crevalle jack but is a much smaller fish, averaging 2 pounds in weight. It lacks the dark blotch on the pectoral fins typical of the crevalle jack. This species occurs along the Atlantic Coast north to Cape Cod.

The BANDED RUDDERFISH is a silvery brown or blue member of the jack family found along the Atlantic Coast from New England to Virginia; it rarely exceeds 18 inches in length and a weight of 4 pounds. Young rudderfish, abundant in the northern part of the range, are marked by 5 or 6 dark vertical bars. They travel in schools following larger fishes and fishing boats. The PILOT FISH also follows boats, but is found in deeper offshore waters than the rudderfish. The pilot fish is bluish in color with indistinct vertical bars; it differs from other members of the family in lacking a spiny dorsal fin. Pilot fish, which grows to a length of 24 inches, inhabits waters off the southeastern coast. Both rudderfish and pilot fish are believed by fishermen to lead larger fishes to food.

Some members of the jack family have a body that is almost circular when viewed from the side. The LOOKDOWN is about as deep as it is long and has a high, sloping "forehead." It is a small fish under 12 inches in length and weighing less than a pound. In color it is light blue-green with iridescent silvery sides; the first rays of the posterior dorsal and anal fins are prolonged into tapering tips. The lookdown is an Atlantic Coast species most common south of Chesapeake Bay; it is caught from bridges, piers, and channel banks. The AT-LANTIC MOONFISH is a similar fish of the same size and range, but its profile is not quite so high and the fins lack the tapering tips. Young moonfish are common in summer in the vicinity of New York.

Best-known member of the family is the POMPANO, a seafood delicacy and a popular shallow-water game fish. It is a light-colored fish with blue back and silvery sides tinted with yellow; the tail fin is blue and yellow. In the pompano the spiny dorsal fin is reduced to a series of very small spines.

The pompano lacks teeth and as a result feeds on invertebrates and small fishes. The average individual is 18 inches or less in length and weighs under 2 pounds. This species is common along the Atlantic Coast south of the Carolinas. PERMIT, or round pompano, is a similar fish of the same waters; the fins are a more dusky blue and the fish grows to a slightly larger size with a maximum of 20 pounds. Two other species of pompano occur on the Pacific Coast.

The Barracuda Family

This is a family of voracious fishes notorious because of the attacks of one species—the great barracuda—on swimmers. There are over twenty species in the family, common to all warm seas; five species range northward into the United States on both the Atlantic and Pacific coasts. A barracuda is a beautifully streamlined fish with the body proportions of a pike. The dorsal fins are small and widely separated from each other; the soft-rayed dorsal and the anal fin are located far back on the body near the tail. Barracuda flesh is edible but at times may be poisonous because of toxic organisms on which it has fed.

The GREAT BARRACUDA ranges north along the Atlantic Coast to the Carolinas. This killer among fishes has the lines of an underwater missile with pointed head, long cylindrical body, and tapering tail. It is a light blue fish with silvery sides that are at times indistinctly barred or spotted. The large mouth is full of sharp, knifelike teeth. The bite of a barracuda is straight and clean, made by a single strike so swift and powerful it can cut a fish in two or easily sever an arm or a leg; the bite of a shark leaves a more curved edge. Most barracudas are under 5 feet in length and weigh about 10 pounds, although large individuals up to 10 feet have been caught. Pursuing schools of such fishes as mullet and grunt, the barracuda will dart suddenly into their midst to make a kill. It is a solitary and fearless hunter tackling prey much larger than itself with directness and lightning speed. A PACIFIC BARRACUDA, similar in appearance and habits, is a smaller and less vicious fish usually under 12 inches in length. This species is found from Monterey southward along the California coast where it is considered a desirable food fish. The NORTHERN BARRACUDA, also known as sennet, is a smaller and more northern species found along the Atlantic Coast as far north as Cape Cod. It is an olive-green fish usually under 12 inches in length. This miniature predator hovers over sandy bottoms in bays, where it preys on smaller fishes, but it is harmless to man.

The Tarpon Family

Of the three American species in this family, the ATLANTIC TARPON, otherwise known as the silver king, is the most familiar. This tarpon is an iridescent silvery fish with greenish-blue tints on the back. The body is protected by extremely large cycloid scales often measuring 3 inches in diameter and used in making novelties and jewelry. The head terminates in a broad mouth with an out-thrust lower jaw armed with small teeth. A distinctive feature is the extension of the last ray of the dorsal fin into a long tapering filament. This is thought to be of use in directing the tremendous leaps typical of a tarpon. The filament is concave on the lower side and can adhere to the fish's body; this bends the dorsal fin in such a way as to determine the direction of the tarpon's fall. An average tarpon is 4 to 5 feet in length and weighs up to 30 pounds; large fish are occasionally caught that are 7 feet long and weigh as much as 200 pounds. Tarpon is carnivorous, feeding on smaller species such as mullet. It is a year-round game fish in Florida, being found offshore as well as in mouths of rivers and bays. During summer it wanders northward to the Carolinas. Tarpon has little food value and is primarily a trophy fish. As a fighter it is unexcelled, dramatically leaping high out of the water when hooked.

The Tarpon Family is represented by the famous Atlantic tarpon (1). The Dolphin Family includes the common dolphin (2). The Barracuda Family includes the notorious great barracuda (3). Figures 1 and 3 adapted from Francesca La Monte, "North American Game Fishes"; 2 from Hashime Murayama in National Geographic Magazine.

The Bonefish Family

This family of herringlike fishes has only one American member. BONEFISH is a sleek silvery fish found in warm waters northward on the Atlantic Coast to Cape Cod and to San Diego on the Pacific Coast. The long and slender body is covered with small scales; a single large dorsal fin located midway along the back lacks the elongated tapering ray found in the tarpon. Bonefish is a bottom-feeder subsisting on crabs, mollusks, and other small invertebrates. The mouth located on the underside of the snout is an adaptation for this type of feeding. Bonefish is usually under 36 inches in length and less than 5 pounds in weight. Bonefish often come with the tide into shallow water over sand bars and mud flats where they reveal their presence by stirring up the water as they grub for buried worms. This is a wily as well as a speedy fish, as is indicated by the scientific name *albula vulpes,* which means "white fox." As a result it is a prized game fish considered by many the best fighter for its size among all the saltwater fishes.

The Dolphin Family

Unfortunately, the word "dolphin" is used for two completely unrelated animals. It is the common name for a kind of porpoise, which is a sea-going mammal; it is also the name of a fast-swimming and streamlined fish of warm seas. The DOLPHIN occurs on the Atlantic Coast from Florida to the Carolinas, and on the Pacific Coast from California to Oregon. A live dolphin is a gorgeously colored fish, blue and green and yellow, with a deep blue dorsal fin and a yellow tail fin. These brilliant colors fade to a nondescript gray soon after the dolphin is caught. In profile a dolphin has a high "forehead" and an enlarged forward end to its body, which tapers gracefully to a deeply forked tail fin. Dolphins are usually under 36 inches in length; a record individual caught in Hawaii was 5 feet long and weighed 67 pounds. Dolphins are such accomplished swimmers that they pursue and feed on the speedy flying fishes, their favorite prey. When hooked, a dolphin leaps into the air, tarpon fashion.

The Billfish Family

Members of this and the following family, the swordfish, differ from all the preceding species in having the upper jaw

141

The Billfish Family is noted for two of its game fishes: the blue marlin (1) and the Atlantic sailfish (2). The Swordfish Family includes the giant swordfish (3). Figures 1 and 2 adapted from Maynard Reece in Life Magazine; 3 from Hashime Murayama in National Geographic Magazine.

prolonged into a long spear or sword. The billfish family bears a cylindrical spear at the tip of the head; the body is covered with scales and possesses ventral fins. This family includes six species in the United States common on both the Atlantic and Pacific coasts. Among them are the most prized of all trophy game fishes: marlin and sailfish.

The WHITE MARLIN has a dark-blue back and long dorsal fin; the latter extends from the head almost to the tail, with a bluntly rounded forward edge. The ventral fins, situated below the pectorals, are reduced to slender and elongated appendages. This is a rather small marlin, usually weighing 50 to 100 pounds although a maximum size of 9 feet and a weight of 160 pounds has been recorded. White marlin ranges from Florida to New England. The best fishing for this species is in midsummer off the northern shores, in winter and spring off the Florida coast. Sometimes solitary, at other times in groups, white marlin is caught a few miles from shore to 20 miles out at sea. In the north this species is most frequently caught off Martha's Vineyard, Massachusetts; Montauk, New York; and Ocean City, Maryland. The BLUE MARLIN is a larger species. It has the same dark-blue back and long dorsal fin, but the forward edge of the latter rises to a sharper point. A coppery color often tints the upper sides, which also may reveal faint vertical stripes. Blue marlin is the most popular game fish of southern Atlantic waters; it is most frequently caught off Cuba and the Bahamas and is never very abundant off the Florida coast. An average individual weighs about 200 pounds. Giant individuals have reportedly measured 20 feet in length and weighed 1000 pounds. STRIPED MARLIN is a Pacific Coast species usually caught in California waters. It is the same color and has the same dorsal and ventral fin characteristics as the other marlins, but it has a shorter spear and is marked by pale lavender stripes that extend from the back to the belly. This species reaches a weight of 250 pounds.

The ATLANTIC SAILFISH is readily recognized by its high sail-like dorsal fin. Like the marlin it carries a spear at the tip of its nose. The dorsal fin and back are a royal blue; the rest of the body is silvery with vertical rows of small dark spots. The dark slender ventral fins are even more elongated than those of the marlins. Sailfish make use of their crescent-shaped and deeply forked tail fin to skip along the surface as if sailing on the water. This species is common along the surface as if sailing on the water. This species is common in tropical Atlantic waters but also occurs at times as far north as New York. It is a fish of the open sea, with flying fishes as its favorite food. When in the midst of a school of fishes, a sailfish uses its spear in beating them unconscious before eating them. Sailfish reach a maximum length of 8 feet and a weight of 100 pounds. A PACIFIC SAILFISH of similar appearance and habits but of slightly larger size occurs along the southern California coast.

The Swordfish Family

The single species in this unusual family is a wide-ranging fish found in both the Atlantic and Pacific oceans. The flavor of its flesh has made the swordfish a prized catch for centuries; the story of swordfishing dates back to the Mediterranean peoples of over two thousand years ago. Little change has been made by the modern fishermen in the method of catching swordfish since the ancient Greeks likewise pursued it with harpoons. The SWORDFISH is shaped like an oversized mackerel; the body is thickest at the shoulder region and tapers gracefully to a tail that is reinforced by a keel on either side. The forward end of the swordfish has an upper jaw prolonged into a double-edged sword 3 to 5 feet in length. Terminating the body is the large crescent-shaped tail that can propel the huge body through the water at remarkable speed. A single large dorsal fin slanting backward is located above the pectoral fins; there are no ventral fins. In front of the tail fin, on the upper as well as the lower side, is a small finlet. The body lacks scales and is a coppery blue with dusky fins;

the eyes are unusually large and have a blue iris. A swordfish rivals many sharks in size; an average individual weighs 200 to 400 pounds, but reported maximum lengths approach 16 feet with corresponding weights of over 1000 pounds.

A swordfish makes use of its nasal appendage for both offense and defense. Rising below a school of mackerel, this "gladiator of the sea" swings its lethal sword from side to side killing or injuring many fishes on which it afterward feeds. Swordfish can also use this weapon in defense after being harpooned. Numerous authentic tales are on record of small boats whose sides have been pierced by a charging swordfish. Most swordfishing is done in specially equipped boats by skilled harpooners. The best fishing grounds on the Atlantic Coast are off Nova Scotia; Block Island, Rhode Island; and Montauk, New York. The fish are caught during the summer months. In the Pacific swordfishing is at its best during the early winter months. The flesh is so highly prized that the demand for swordfish far exceeds the American supply. Much of the commercial catch comes from Canada, Peru, Chile, and Japan.

The adult halibut has both eyes on the upper, pigmented side of its body (top); the underside (bottom), usually unpigmented is eyeless.   American Museum of Natural History, New York

Chapter Six

Food from the Sea

From the point of view of the sport fishermen, the important members of the fish population are those spectacular, often giant-sized species that fight dramatically for their lives when caught on a hook. We have made the acquaintance of some of these: tarpon and tuna, sea bass and sailfish, marlin and dolphin. We have also met the less impressive species that make up the catch of the fisherman who drops a line from a bridge or pier, or fishes from a boat near shore for bluefish, drum, mackerel, bonefish, or pompano. These fishes are often exciting adversaries, yet they are also commercially important food fishes as the annual catch of many millions of pounds testifies.

The wealth of the sea is not measured primarily in terms of game fishes. To millions of people who have relied for centuries on fish as a staple part of their diet and to the thousands of professional fishermen who brave the dangers of the sea to harvest this crop, the most important species are the less colorful and, for the most part, smaller fishes such as herring and menhaden, cod and haddock, flounder and halibut. They and their relatives make up a few families that constitute the major part of the commercial harvest from the sea; families that provide an annual haul of over a half a billion pounds for use as food and a billion pounds more for industrial uses such as for fertilizer.

The *Herring Family* can be recognized by the single soft-rayed dorsal fin. Very similar in appearance is the *Smelt Family,* also with the single fin but having in addition a small adipose fin between the dorsal and tail fins as in the salmon family. The *Cod Family* includes species with a variety of dorsal fins: some have three, some two, and some a single dorsal fin. With few exceptions, members of the family have a barbel under the lower jaw. The several *Flounder Families* are characterized by a single long dorsal fin, but the most distinctive feature is the thin flattened body with both eyes on the same side. The food fishes in these families are primarily cold-water inhabitants of the north Atlantic and Pacific oceans and are especially abundant off the northeastern coast of the United States.

The Herring Family

The *Herring Family* includes over twenty American species common to both our Atlantic and Pacific waters. Members of the family are small, streamlined fishes whose bodies are covered with small cycloid scales. The single dorsal fin, without spines, is situated in the middle of the back; the tail fin is deeply forked; and a special row of spiny scales along the midline of the belly gives the underside a saw-toothed appearance. The pointed head terminates in a large mouth that is either toothless or armed with very small teeth. A herring obtains most of its food as it swims through the water with open mouth sucking in minute plankton organisms that happen to be in its path. This food is strained out of the water by sievelike gill rakers in the throat. Apart from their importance to man, the herrings form a vital link in the food-chain of the sea (see p. 37), being the basic converters of minute plants and animals into flesh. In the endless cycle wherein big fishes eat smaller fishes, the herrings form the main diet of the larger mackerel, cod, and other carnivorous species. The Herring Family includes herring, sardine, and menhaden, which spend their entire lives in the sea, and shad and alewife, which migrate into freshwater habitats to spawn.

The ATLANTIC HERRING is the most plentiful fish in the sea and at the same time the most valuable. It is a greenish or steely blue fish with gleaming silvery sides often tinted with gold. One-year old herring 3 to 5 inches in length are marketed as sardines. By the time they are four years old, herring reach a length of 10 inches. Individuals that live to an age of 20 years attain a length of 18 inches. Atlantic herring are found in cold waters from New England and Canada in the north Atlantic to Great Britain. For centuries it has been the leading food fish of the world; herring fisheries have been vital to the economy of eastern Europe since the twelfth century. Sardine canning plants are numerous along the coast of Maine. Today the annual yield along the New England coast is over 200 million pounds. It has been estimated that the annual world catch amounts to more than two billion *tons!*

Herring swim in tremendous schools, sometimes near the surface where their presence is indicated by the predatory sea birds, sometimes in deeper water where many fall prey to cod and haddock. All members of a school are usually of the same size and age. These schools venture inshore during the summer months, retire to deeper offshore waters in winter. The British biologist T. H. Huxley has estimated that herring schools contain at least 500 million fish per square mile, and schools often extend for many miles. Herring spawn in autumn off the New England coast; the heavy, adhesive eggs sink to the bottom and adhere in clumps to seaweeds and rocks. Ichthyologists have discovered that off the British coast the peak of spawning coincides with the period of full moon. In the

United States most of the herring catch is canned as sardines or made into fish meal. In Europe many herring are salted, pickled, or otherwise cured and are consumed as "kippered herring" or "kippers."

Similar in appearance to the Atlantic herring is the SPAN-ISH SARDINE, a smaller and more southern species, usually less than 6 inches in length. Found from Cape Cod to Florida, it is of little economic importance except for use as bait. The PACIFIC SARDINE, or pilchard, the size of the Atlantic herring, has distinctive dark spots along its sides. A half billion pounds are harvested annually to be converted into fish oil and fish meal.

MENHADEN is a silvery fish of variable coloring: green, blue, gray, or brown. It is a more chunky fish than herring and marked by a large spot behind the upper margin of the gill cover. Menhaden are usually under 12 inches in length but many reach a maximum of 20 inches. Menhaden are commonly found in schools near shore along the entire Atlantic Coast. They spawn in summer; the eggs are buoyant and hatch rapidly, within two days, at a water temperature of 72° F. This species is so rich in oil that it is unfit for use as food. Industrially the oil is extremely valuable, and after the oil is extracted, the remains are processed as fertilizer. One billion pounds of this seemingly insignificant member of the herring family are converted into such products annually. In fact this modest herring relative is the most valuable industrial resource of the sea.

Two species of the herring family—alewife and shad—are often considered freshwater fishes for they are caught while entering streams and lakes to spawn. The ALEWIFE is a grayish green fish with silvery sides and belly. It is known by a variety of other names: golden shad, skipjack, and sawbelly. Alewives reach a maximum length of 15 inches and weigh less than 1 pound. They are found in streams and ponds from New England to the Carolinas; some have become landlocked

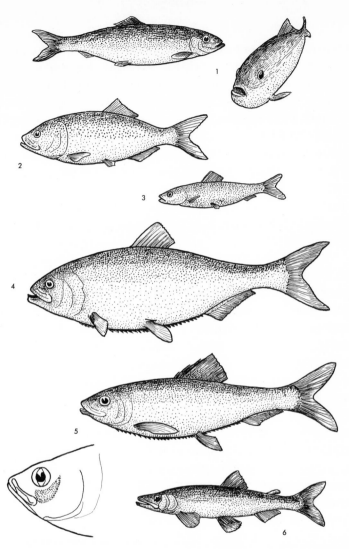

The Herring Family includes the common Atlantic herring (1), menhaden (2), Spanish sardine (3), shad (4), alewife (5). The related Smelt Family includes the common smelt (6). Figures 2 and 3 from C. M. Breder, "Field Book of Marine Fishes of the Atlantic Coast"; 4, 5, 6 adapted from Francesca La Monte, "North American Game Fishes."

in the Great Lakes. After 3 or 4 years spent at sea, alewives enter the coastal rivers making their way upstream to ponds and lakes, usually to the place where they were born. In New England the alewife run begins in April and continues through May. The upstream migration usually takes place during daylight hours. Thousands of squirming silvery fish crowd the small tributaries leading into coastal ponds. Here they are caught in dipnets as fast as fishermen can scoop them from the water. During spawning, each female scatters some 100,000 heavy, adhesive eggs that become attached to stones and vegetation on the bottom. The eggs hatch in one week, and the young alewives spend the first summer feeding on plankton in the streams and ponds. The return trip to the sea begins in midsummer and lasts through November. At this time the young alewives are 2 to 6 inches in length. After spawning, some of the adults remain until December in their freshwater homes, and many of them return the following season to spawn a second time. Alewives are salted and smoked for eating; the canned roe is sold as a delicacy. Many of the fish are ground into fertilizer. The annual catch has been greatly reduced in recent years by stream pollution, the construction of dams, and overfishing.

SHAD are similar in appearance to alewives but grow to a larger size, with an average weight of 2 to 3 pounds and an occasional maximum weight of 10 pounds. Thus shad are the largest members of the herring family. Shad differ from alewives in having dark spots behind the gills and a notched upper jaw. The silvery area beneath the eye deeper than it is long; in the alewife this area is longer than it is deep. Shad enter coastal streams from New England to Florida; they are particularly abundant in the Potomac River. After a sojourn of 3 or 4 years at sea, they return for their spawning run upstream; the males lead the procession, soon followed by the females. During their spring run shad, like alewives, are caught by the thousands in nets and seines. But stream pollution and overfishing have reduced the number of shad also.

The Smelt Family

This, too, is a family of saltwater fishes that enters streams and ponds to spawn, in some cases becoming landlocked and never returning to the sea. Ten species occur in the United States on both the Atlantic and Pacific coasts. Along the Atlantic Coast smelt are found from New England to Virginia, with landlocked populations in Lake Ontario, Lake Champlain, and several New England lakes. Smelt is a small streamlined fish superficially like herring but, in possessing an adipose fin, also like salmon and trout. The body is covered with ctenoid scales; the belly lacks the saw-tooth ventral scales of the alewife and shad.

The AMERICAN SMELT is a somewhat transparent, olive-green fish with silvery belly and often with a silvery lengthwise stripe along each side. Smelt leave the sea and enter coastal streams soon after the ice melts, sometimes as early as February. Most of the fish participating in this spawning run have spent two years at sea; their average length is 6 to 7 inches with a maximum of 14 inches. Spawning usually takes place at night in streams with a sandy or stony bottom. Groups of males and females collect over riffles where the current is rapid and release the eggs and milt. Smelt eggs are adhesive, sticking to stones on the bottom and hatching in a few weeks into small fish a quarter of an inch in length. These drift downstream, many of them falling prey to salmon. Those that survive remain in fresh water for the summer feeding chiefly on plankton, insects, worms, and other small aquatic animals, and growing to a length of one to two inches. Landlocked smelts live·in the depths of clear lakes but in winter come to the surface where they are often caught through holes in the ice. The flesh of a smelt has a delicate flavor but is too oily for the average taste. If a wick is inserted in the mouth of a dried smelt, it will burn like a candle; in fact one local name for smelt is candlefish. The oil of smelt is sometimes used as a substitute for cod liver oil.

153

The Codfish Family

This family of cold-water fishes is represented by over twenty species in the waters of both our Atlantic and Pacific coasts. Cod and its relatives are elongated fishes with small cycloid scales. The chin bears a single barbel, with the one exception of the silver hake. The number and shape of the dorsal and anal fins differ in various species of the family. Three dorsal and two anal fins are characteristic of cod, tomcod, pollock, and haddock. Two dorsal and a single anal fin are features of hake and burbot, a freshwater species inhabiting streams and lakes of eastern United States. Cusk has a single dorsal and a single anal fin. Most of the species are bottom-dwellers with carnivorous or omnivorous appetites.

ATLANTIC COD is a dull-colored fish varying in color from gray-green to reddish brown; the sides are spotted with yellow or brown, the belly is light gray or tan, and the lateral line is a lighter color than the rest of the body. Three approximately equal-sized dorsal fins without spines extend from head to tail fin. There are two anal fins of which the forward one is slightly larger than the other. Small ventral fins are located in front of and below the pectoral fins. An average cod is 2 to 3 feet in length and weighs under 10 pounds. A record individual measures 6 feet in length and weighs up to 200 pounds. Cod are voracious eaters roaming in packs over the sea bottom, consuming mollusks, sea urchins, starfish, crustaceans, worms, and—their favorite morsel—herring. Cod are a migratory fish abundant at times off the New England coast.

Cod has played an important role in the early history of the United States. The abundance of cod off the Newfoundland Banks was a chief reason for the establishment of English colonies in North America. A wooden model of a huge cod still hangs in the Massachusetts State House, placed there in 1784 to honor the fish that contributed so much to early New England economy. Cod is a valuable commercial fish because of its flavor and its suitability for salting and processing. It is also an excellent source of vitamin D in the familiar cod liver oil. It seems a paradox that this "sunshine vitamin" should be stored up in an animal that spends all its life in the dark depths of the sea. Cod, together with its relatives had-

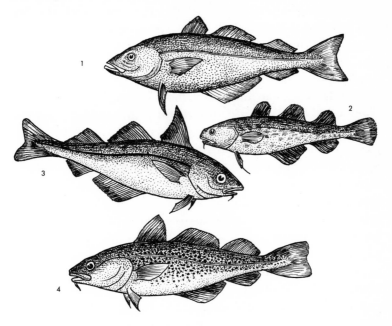

The Codfish Family includes such valuable food fishes as pollock (1), tomcod (2), haddock (3) and cod (4). Figures 1 and 2 adapted from Francesca La Monte, "North American Game Fishes"; 3 and 4 from Hashime Murayama in National Geographic Magazine.

dock, pollock, and hake, are the chief catch of party fishing boats off the New England coast.

The ATLANTIC TOMCOD is a more southern fish found from New England south to Virginia. It is olive-green, tinged with yellow and marked by dark blotches on the side. The narrow ventral fins have a prolonged extension on their forward edge. Smaller than the Atlantic cod, its average length is 15 inches and its weight rarely more than 2 pounds. Tomcod is a shoal-water fish, especially abundant in harbors and bays where it is popular as both a sport and a food fish. It is not sufficiently abundant to be of commercial value. Tomcod is also called frostfish because of its early winter habit of ascending coastal streams to spawn; such spawning individuals have been found sixty miles upstream in the Kennebec River of Maine. A PACIFIC TOMCOD, of similar appearance and habits, occurs on the west coast from California to Alaska.

HADDOCK is an important food fish whose flavor is generally considered superior to cod. Haddock differs from cod in being dark gray with silvery sides and belly and in having a conspicuous black lateral line and a higher first dorsal fin. A dark patch usually occurs above the pectoral fin. A specimen of average size weighs 3 to 4 pounds; the maximum length is about 3 feet and weight 24 pounds. Haddock is found along our northeastern coast south to New Jersey. Its feeding habits are similar to those of cod. Although less widely distributed and less abundant than cod, the annual catch is much greater. The popular "finnan haddie" of Scotland is smoked haddock.

POLLOCK is a bluish or greenish brown fish with yellow-gray sides and lighter gray underparts. The lateral line is conspicuously white, and the tail is more distinctly forked than in either cod or haddock. The average weight is between 4 and 12 pounds; larger individuals reach a length of 4 feet and weigh as much as 40 pounds. Pollock is a gluttonous bottom-feeder especially destructive of young cod.

SILVER HAKE, or whiting, differs from the preceding members of the family by having only two dorsal fins and a single anal fin. The second dorsal fin is very long, about half the length of the body; the anal fin is equally long. Silver hake is a brownish fish with a silvery glint to the entire body; the chin lacks the barbel type of other members of the cod family. The pikelike head terminates in a large mouth armed with strong teeth. An average length is 12 to 20 inches and weight under 5 pounds. Silver hake is a voracious eater, preying on smaller fish. It is a migratory species found in large

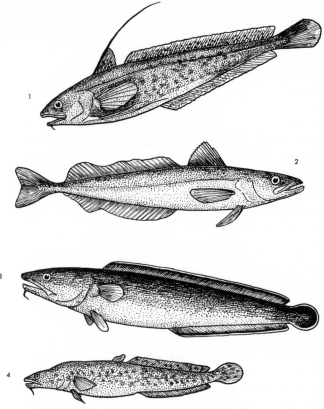

The Codfish Family also includes squirrel hake (1), silver hake (2), cusk (3), and the freshwater burbot (4). Figures 1, 2, 3 adapted from Hashime Murayama in National Geographic Magazine; 4 from Francesca La Monte, "North American Game Fishes."

schools that concentrate over sandy and pebbly bottoms. Although found from New England to Florida, silver hake is caught most frequently from Cape Cod to Virginia. The PACIFIC HAKE, found from California to Washington, is an iron-gray fish with silvery sides and has similar habits to those of the eastern silver hake. SQUIRREL HAKE, also known as red hake or ling, is found from New England to North Carolina. The back and upper sides are brown or olive-gray, the lower sides are silvery. Like the silver hake it has two dorsal fins, the second dorsal being extremely long and low. The anterior dorsal fin has an elongated and tapering forward ray. Another distinctive feature is the shape of the ventral fins, which are long and slender, tapering to thread-like extremities. Squirrel hake is usually under 30 inches in length and weighs less than 8 pounds. This hake is commercially important in the northern part of its range; much of the catch is converted into pet and poultry food.

CUSK is a dark gray or brown fish, ranging southward from the Arctic along the Atlantic Coast to Cape Cod. It resembles a squirrel hake in general shape, with typical ventral fins, but has only a single long, low dorsal fin. The dorsal, tail, and anal fins are distinctive in their black margins neatly edged in white. Cusk prefers rocky bottoms at depth of over 60 feet. An average individual is 18 to 20 inches in length, but large individuals attain 40 inches and may weigh as much as 27 pounds.

BURBOT, the freshwater member of the codfish family, is a dusky mottled fish with two dorsal fins: the forward one small, the posterior long and low. The chin bears a single but prominent barbel. The average individual is 15 inches in length and weighs less than 1 pound. Large burbots reach a length of 30 inches and a weight of 10 pounds. This cod relative lives in cold streams and lakes of the Great Lakes region eastward to New England. It feeds on smaller fish such as smelt and sucker. Burbot is of only slight sport or commercial importance.

The Flounder Family

Exploring the world of nature leads to many surprises, but one of the most fascinating in the realm of sea life is the way the flounder becomes adapted for its benthic way of life. Flounders, which are classified into several different families, include flounder, sole, sand dab, and halibut. All are extremely thin, flattened fishes with a circular or elliptical outline. Over five hundred species are widely distributed from the Arctic to the tropics. In the United States the group is represented by over sixty species, half of which occur on the Atlantic Coast and half on the Pacific Coast. All are carnivorous fishes scouring the bottom for a variety of invertebrates such as crabs, shrimps, lobsters, mussels, and clams; they also prey on any smaller fishes that come within reach.

When born, a flounder resembles a normal fish and swims in the usual upright position. But while yet less than one inch in length it turns on its side, some species "reclining" on the right side, other species on the left. Then a remarkable change takes place. The eye on the lower side moves across the top of the head to take its place beside the eye on the upper side. In fact, the skull may also become twisted and the mouth assume a lopsided position. The lower side, in the absence of light, becomes yellowish white; the upper side becomes pigmented in colors and patterns that display a marked similarity to the surroundings. The air bladder also disappears. This entire transformation takes place during the first six to twelve weeks of the flounder's life. Such changes do not make the fishes any more attractive by our standards, but they do adapt them to a specialized way of living. Flounders retain this horizontal position when they swim, undulating in an up-and-down movement rather than using the customary means of fish propulsion. The side to which a flounder leans is determined by its heredity, which is fixed for all members of a species. The exception is the starry flounder of the Pacific Coast, which seems to be undecided about which side shall be uppermost. About half the population have the eyes on the left side, half on the right. Common left-eyed species include the summer flounder, California halibut, and the Pacific sand dab. Common right-eyed species are the winter flounder, Atlantic halibut, and the American sole. The American sole is of little commercial value; so-called filet of sole is actually filet of flounder.

SUMMER FLOUNDER, also known as northern fluke, a left-eyed species, is brown or grayish in color and marked with dark spots each surrounded by a white margin. The flounder can assume other colors, which seems to indicate an unusual ability to make itself inconspicuous. On a red background, summer flounder becomes reddish in color; on a blue background it becomes bluish. An average individual is 15 to 20 inches in length and weighs under 5 pounds. Larger specimens measure up to 48 inches and weigh as much as 26 pounds. Summer flounder is more predatory than most of its relatives, pursuing smaller fish to the surface and often jumping out of the water to catch them.

WINTER FLOUNDER, also known as blackjack, has the eyes and pigmentation on the right side. This side is dark olive-green or reddish brown, sometimes spotted with red. It is a small flounder with an average size of 15 inches and a weight of less than 2 pounds. Large individuals attain a maximum weight of 5 pounds. Winter flounder is abundant from southern New England to Chesapeake Bay where it is caught in late winter and early spring. Its favorite habitat is deep-water bays where it is a popular sport fish as well as a valuable food fish.

Two right-eyed flounders commonly caught off the northern Atlantic Coast are the witch flounder and the yellowtail flounder. The WITCH FLOUNDER, or gray sole, is a grayish brown fish found north of Cape Cod; its average length is 24 inches and weight is 4 pounds. It is usually caught at depths of over 60 feet but has been brought up from a depth of a mile. This species is commercially unimportant. The YELLOWTAIL FLOUNDER, or rusty dab, is a brown or olive-gray fish tinged with red and marked by scattered reddish brown spots. On the underside, the tail is yellowish as are the edges of the dorsal and anal fins. This flounder occurs

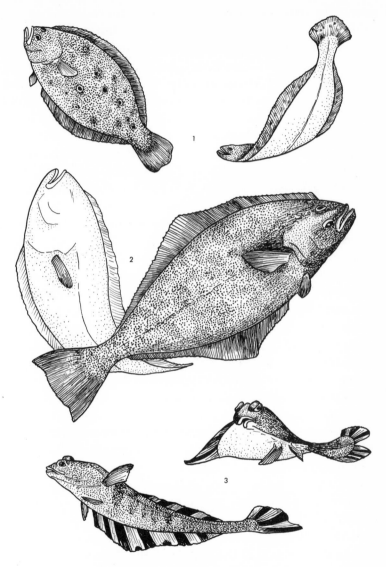

Among the flatfishes are the summer flounder (1), halibut (2), and starry flounder (3). All figures adapted from Hashime Murayama in National Geographic Magazine.

at moderate depths from New England to Virginia; it is of about the same size as the witch flounder.

The STARRY FLOUNDER, or California flounder, is found along the entire Pacific Coast; it is a brownish fish with colorful fins. The dorsal and anal fin are marked by alternate vertical bands of orange, and similar horizontal markings decorate the tail fin. Star-shaped tubercles scattered over the body give this flounder its common name. This is the species that has not made up its mind as to whether the eyes should be on the right side or the left. This species attains a weight of 20 pounds but averages much less. It is often found partly buried in the muddy bottom watching for prey with its projecting frog-like eyes. This flounder is one of the several species that make up the annual commercial catch of the Pacific Coast.

The halibut is the largest of the flounders. ATLANTIC HALIBUT is a species of northern seas, found along our Atlantic Coast south to New Jersey. This is a right-eyed flounder with dark gray or olive-brown upper side, and white lower side. Atlantic halibut has a single long continuous dorsal fin and a long anal fin; the small ventral fins are located actually in front of the pectoral fins. It lives in deep water, from several hundred to several thousand feet below the surface. Average individuals are 4 to 6 feet long, weigh 50 to 200 pounds. The largest individuals are caught in deeper water; a record size, that of a specimen caught off the Massachusetts coast reached 9 feet in length and weighed 625 pounds. Halibut is a voracious feeder on smaller fish which they hunt in roving groups. An excellent food fish, this species is becoming less abundant. In New England, the commercial catch has decreased during recent years. A related PACIFIC HALIBUT on the west coast is also an important food fish. The CALIFORNIA HALIBUT is a left-eyed fish of mottled greenish brown. It is found from San Francisco southward.

The carnivorous moray eels are the villains of the tropical underwater paradise, hiding amid the rocks and coral and striking like rattlesnakes at passing prey.

Marineland of Florida

Chapter Seven

Colorful Fishes
of Tropical Seas

The peninsula of Florida projects southward toward the Bahamas and the Caribbean Sea, bringing a tip of the United States close to the warm waters of the tropics. Because of this, Florida provides a home for many unusual plants and animals that have migrated northward from the tropics. Here are coconut palms and bamboo, lime trees and mangoes; manatees and crocodiles, flamingoes and ibis. Likewise the waters off the Florida coast offer suitable habitats for many tropical species of fishes occurring nowhere else in the United States.

We have already become acquainted with some of the northern fishes that are caught by sportsmen or hauled aboard commercial fishing boats. We will now turn our attention to some fishes off the southern Florida coast, many of which reveal an arresting variety of form, coloring, and adaptations to a special way of life. Until recently one had to be content with seeing the colorful world of tropical fishes indistinctly from above the surface of the water. Today it is possible to don snorkel tubes or aqualungs and meet the fishes face-to-face in their natural surroundings. Let us imagine for the moment that we can enter this underseas world and swim about with its inhabitants.

This tropical wonderland could be entered quickly by diving from a pier or wading out from a sandy beach. But instead, we can meet these fish by visiting a completely underwater state park. Off the eastern edge of Key Largo, near Key West, lies a coral reef twenty-one miles long and four miles wide; it has long been known for the abundance and variety of its marine life. Conservationists feared that this unusual wild life area might be exploited and vanish before it could be adequately protected. To prevent this, interested Floridians campaigned so successfully that in March, 1960, President Eisenhower proclaimed the area *Key Largo Coral Reef Preserve*. As the three-mile limit cuts lengthwise through the reef area so that some of it belongs to the state of Florida, Florida also gave the area a name: *John Pennekamp Coral Reef State Park* in honor of the conservationist who helped bring the park into existence. The 50,000 acres constitute the first and only American underwater park—a paradise for scuba divers and marine biologists.

As we sink slowly through crystal-clear water, we find ourselves on bottom at a depth of 15 or 20 feet. All around us are great mounds of many-hued coral separated by gullies of white sand. Each coral cliff is honeycombed with crevices in which fishes are hiding or from which they are constantly darting in search of food. Schools of fishes swim by in military precision, pausing to nibble our fingers or stare at the invaders from another world. Most of the fishes are less than 12 inches in length, with saucer-thin bodies and extravagantly fashioned fins; they exhibit a wide range of colors from black and blue through browns and greens to golden yellow and fiery orange. They are not built for speed; instead they are equipped with fins that enable them to maneuver with agility and escape their enemies by quick turns and sudden sallies into narrow crevices. Among these dwellers of the reefs we will find fishes with such strange but appropriate names as butterfly fish, surgeonfish, parrot fish, squirrelfish, and triggerfish.

The Grunt Family

Many of the common inhabitants of the coral gardens are members of the grunt family, chunky fishes with elevated backs and short deep bodies, related to the snappers. The name grunt comes from the peculiar sounds made by grinding the pharyngeal teeth together. Grunts are spiny-rayed fishes, with the spiny portion of the dorsal fin continuous with the soft-rayed portion; the tail fin is deeply forked, and the ventral fins are placed far forward beneath the pectoral fins. The mouth has a startling bright red interior displayed effectively as the grunts charge each other with open mouth. They are nocturnal fishes, feeding at night on crabs, shrimps, worms, and mollusks. Most species are 12 to 18 inches in length and rarely weigh over 3 pounds. Some are important local food fish, being the fish used in the "grits and grunts" diet of Key West natives.

There are sixteen different kinds of grunt in Florida waters, with a few additional species on the Pacific Coast. The SPANISH GRUNT, or gray grunt, is a dull silvery gray fish with indistinct horizontal stripes and yellow fins; it sometimes assumes a color pattern of gold stripes. A native of the West Indies, the Spanish grunt reaches Florida as the northern limit of its range. The FRENCH GRUNT, or yellow grunt, is also a West Indies fish. It is more brightly colored, with horizontal stripes of alternating blue and yellow, and with bright yellow fins. Largest of the grunts is the WHITE GRUNT, a common member of the coral reef community; it reaches a weight of 4 pounds. It is a brassy blue fish with many small somewhat horizontal stripes and blue markings in the head region. This fish can change color to match the surroundings, being dusky as it swims among the coral shadows and turning straw-colored when over a sandy bottom. The white grunt sometimes wanders north to the Carolinas.

The PORKFISH is a conspicuous and common species of the coral reef community. It is in a gay attire of blue and gold horizontal stripes, golden yellow fins, and conspicuous black vertical bars in the head region; one extends from the mouth through the eye to the top of the head, another from the pectoral fin to the forward edge of the dorsal fin. The average weight of a porkfish is 1 pound but a maximum of 2 pounds is sometimes reached. Like the other grunts, porkfish are nocturnal, feeding on shrimp, crab, and other small marine invertebrates.

MARGATE is a pearly gray fish with several widely spaced lengthwise stripes on the upper side; when disturbed it turns a greenish hue. The fins are light olive green, the lips are yellowish, and the open mouth reveals a vermilion interior. Margate, whose range extends south of Florida to Brazil, reaches a length of 24 inches and a weight of 10 pounds, but individuals average less than 2 pounds. Margate lives among rocks and submerged wrecks as well as on coral reefs; its foods consists of algae, mollusks, crustaceans, and small fish. BLACK MARGATE, or pompon, is a somewhat similar fish, pearly gray in color with dusky fins; often there is a dark band beneath the pectoral fins. Black margate grows to considerable size, reaching a length of 36 inches. It hides by day in the holes and grottoes among the coral, emerging at night to feed on small aquatic invertebrates.

PIGFISH is a bluish purple grunt with silvery sides and golden stripes along the back. The dorsal fin is spotted with bronze; the paired fins and the base of the tail are yellow. The sides are marked above the lateral line by oblique stripes, below the lateral line by lengthwise stripes. This member of the family is found not only in the warm reef waters but also at times as far north as New York.

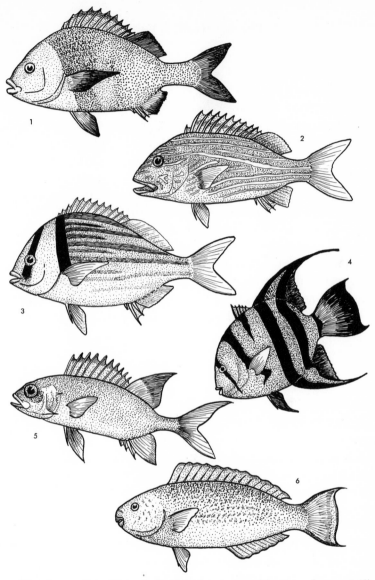

The Grunt Family includes black margate (1), French grunt (2), and porkfish (3). Other families of tropical fishes are represented by spadefish (4), squirrelfish (5), and rainbow parrot fish (6). All figures adapted from Marineland (Florida) material.

The Squirrelfish Family

We see other spiny-rayed fishes swimming about us. Of these, the squirrelfishes are especially conspicuous because of their extremely large eyes, which indicate that this species is a nocturnal animal. When disturbed, these fish chatter noisily, a trait reminding one of the land animals from which the squirrelfishes get their name. Of the nine species in the family, all are found in the south Atlantic region. The COMMON SQUIRRELFISH, a showy fish darting in and out of the coral thickets, is bright red on the back and rosy red on the underside. The fins are also bright red; the dorsal fin has a yellowish base. The forward portion of the dorsal fin has large tough spines that can spread the fin like a fan. This squirrelfish is usually under 12 inches in length; it has a southern range to Brazil. Squirrelfish are active, carnivorous fish feeding at night but hiding by day in crevices of the coral reef. A relative, the RED SQUIRRELFISH, is an important market fish in Hawaii.

The Parrot Fish Family

Some of the brilliantly colored fishes hover close to the coral seeming to browse along its surface as rabbits nibble grass. A closer look reveals that they have a beaklike mouth formed by the fusion of the front teeth. These fishes are suitably named parrot fishes because of this beaklike mouth; over a dozen species live in Florida waters. Parrot fishes scour the rocks and corals snipping off the attached algae and sedentary invertebrates. A common species is the RAINBOW PARROT FISH whose oblong body is covered with large cycloid scales. The blunt head terminates in a greenish blue beak strong enough to bite through a fish hook. It is one of the most brilliantly colored of the reef fishes and also one of the largest, often 36 inches in length. The body is a mixture of green and gold with a rosy breast; the pectoral fins are green, the other fins red with blue margins. The dorsal fin is long and low with very little separation between the spiny and soft-rayed portions. Other species of parrot fish wander northward along the Atlantic Coast; among these is the BLUE PARROT FISH found at times as far north as Chesapeake Bay.

The Spadefish Family

Many of the fishes we encounter in the reef gardens have a circular outline to their saucer-thin bodies. Some of these are spadefishes, a family of only two species, one on the Atlantic and one on the Pacific Coast. The ATLANTIC SPADEFISH usually is striped vertically, the pearly gray body bearing several broad vertical bands of black. But like so many other tropical fishes, it can change its color and pattern at will, sometimes being entirely black, sometimes white. There are two distinct dorsal fins, the forward spiny portion being very small, the posterior portion larger with a conspicuous extension of the first rays. The anal fin also has an elongated anterior ray. This spadefish grows to a length of 24 inches; it is found not only in the warm Florida waters but also as far north as Cape Cod.

The Butterfly Fish Family

Other thin-bodied circular fishes belong to the *Butterfly Fish Family,* which includes a dozen species in the warmer portion of the Atlantic Ocean; among them are the extremely colorful and ornamental angelfishes. The name for the group is appropriate, for these fishes seem to flit about the coral hummocks much like butterflies above a field of flowers. The body is covered with smooth scales, and the small mouth bears frail brushlike teeth suitable only for nibbling at algae and eating small invertebrate animals. Most of the butterfly fishes are under 12 inches in length. They are quick and agile in their movements, darting about with sudden stops and turns. They are also quarrelsome and aggressive, snapping at each other at the least provocation. Some of the species stray as far north as Cape Cod.

The SPOTFIN BUTTERFLY FISH, or common butterfly fish, about 8 inches in length, has a gray body and yellow fins; the forward portion of the dorsal fin is spiny. A distinctive feature is a dark spot on the posterior part of the dorsal fin. Another conspicuous feature is the dark vertical stripe extending from the mouth through the eye to the top of the head. Smaller but similar in appearance is the FOUREYE BUTTERFLY FISH; it, too, has a grayish body but is marked by faint diagonal stripes extending upward and backward above the lateral line. This species also has a black stripe through the eye. A large eye-spot on each side near the base of the tail gives the fish a double-ended appearance and might well confuse a pursuing predator.

Angelfishes are without doubt the most colorful members of the coral reef community. The FRENCH ANGELFISH, also known as the black angelfish, has a small mouth that limits its diet to sedentary aquatic forms of life. It is a dusky fish speckled with gold; the dorsal fin sweeps gracefully backward terminating in a prolonged tip. Dorsal and anal fins are dusky gray becoming darker at the margins. The pectoral fins are yellow, the ventral fins are black. Like the butterfly fishes, angelfishes are extremely agile in maneuvering into narrow spaces, moving easily in and out of crevices in the coral. The QUEEN ANGELFISH is a larger species attaining a length of 24 inches. It is fittingly named "the queen" for it is one of the most beautiful marine fishes of the United States. Its detailed coloring is difficult to describe. Predominantly blue and gold, the queen has blue lips, blue forehead with a dark-blue eye-spot, blue breast, and blue margins to the long tapering dorsal and anal fins. The sides are pearl gray or fawn-colored, speckled with brown. The tapering

The Butterfly Fish Family has such conspicuous members as queen angelfish (1) and spotfin butterfly fish (2). In the Damselfish Family are beau gregory (4), sergeant major (3), and yellowtail demoiselle (5). The doctorfish (6) is a member of the Surgeonfish Family. All figures adapted from Marineland (Florida) material.

flame-yellow tips of the dorsal and anal fins suggest the jet exhaust of an airplane engine.

ROCK BEAUTY, a West Indies species, is relatively rare in the Florida reef community but, when it does occur, is another gem in the tropical wonderland. It is dramatically two-toned, the head and breast being a golden yellow, the remainder of the body a lustrous black. The margins of the black dorsal and anal fins are yellow, as is the entire tail fin. The forward low spiny portion of the dorsal fin and the spines in front of the anal fin are bright red. The rock beauty is usually less than 12 inches in length.

The Damselfish Family

Damselfishes comprise another group of species with thin, compressed bodies and circular outlines; a dozen species inhabit the Florida coast, and two additional species are found off the California coast. The dorsal fin in this family has a forward spiny portion continuous with a short, pointed posterior portion. Damselfishes have the small mouth typical of many reef fishes, suitable for eating only such small aquatic organisms as invertebrates and algae. The body is covered with large, ctenoid scales.

The YELLOWTAIL DAMSELFISH, or yellowtail demoiselle, is an active little fish about 6 inches in length, native to the West Indies with Florida the northernmost limit of its range. The conspicuous color pattern consists of a dark blue back and dorsal fin, shading into golden yellow on the sides and belly. The paired fins and tail fin are yellow. This damselfish feeds chiefly on organic debris that collects among the crevices of the coral and rocks. BEAU GREGORY also has a dark blue back and dorsal fin, with golden-yellow sides and belly. It is the same size as the yellowtail, but the anal fin is yellow instead of black, and the posterior portion of the dorsal fin has a yellow margin instead of being entirely black. This little damselfish is one of the most aggressive members of the coral reef community. It often makes its home in an empty conch shell, which it defends against all intruders regardless of their size. Another member of the family is known as the SERGEANT MAJOR, an obvious reference to its vertical stripes. Schools of this small fish, also 6 inches in length, have been passing by frequently during exploration of the coral reef. Its fins and underside are pearly gray while the back and upper sides bear broad vertical black and yellow stripes. Sergeant majors can change their color rapidly from a dark phase when they are among the rocks to a light phase when over sandy bottoms.

The Surgeonfish Family

Some tropical fishes have developed unique weapons that serve well in offense and defense against their belligerent neighbors. Members of the Surgeon Family, for example, have a built-in stiletto on either side of the tail, similar to a doctor's scalpel, which gives the family its name. This stiletto is attached at its base and fits snugly into a sheath of skin when not in use. When frightened or disturbed, the fish can erect this spine at right angles to the body and pointed forward. It can inflict a fatal wound by sideswiping an adversary or swinging its tail vigorously as a flail. Being quarrelsome, surgeonfishes often injure each other in this way and should be approached cautiously even by swimmers. The elliptical body of these fishes is deep and compressed and covered by such small scales that the skin feels smooth. The dorsal and anal fins are continuous and low. Like the parrot fishes, surgeonfishes are chiefly herbivorous in their feeding habits.

DOCTORFISH is a West Indies species that wanders into the Florida reef community, with some occasionally straying as far north as Cape Cod; the average length of this surgeonfish is 10 inches. The doctorfish is a brownish fish with dark vertical bars on the sides and oblique stripes across the blue and brown dorsal and anal fins. The tail fin is multicolored with vertical striping of yellow and blue. Another member of this family is the BLUE TANG, which grows to a length of 12 inches. This surgeonfish is deep blue in color; the sides bear irregular horizontal stripes of yellow, and the fins are striped with dark blue or black.

The Filefish Family

Triggerfishes and filefishes are another unique group, armed with a dorsal weapon that consists of either three spines or a single large spine. The family includes eighteen species in the United States, the majority found in the Atlantic Ocean. They differ from their reef neighbors in lacking ventral fins; instead, this portion of the body bears a ventral flap of skin that can be erected by means of a long backward-projecting bone within the flap. In the triggerfishes the dorsal spines form an ingenious interlocking mechanism. The first and largest spine locks into position when erect, thus making it an effective weapon. A tendon extends from the third spine to the base of the first spine; it is only by depressing the third spine that the lock which holds the forward spine erect can be broken. Whenever a triggerfish is disturbed, the first spine becomes erect and automatically locked in position. Filefishes have only one dorsal spine and lack the trigger-release mechanism.

The COMMON TRIGGERFISH is a cream-colored or pearly gray fish almost circular in outline; the soft-rayed dorsal fin and the anal fin are relatively short and high. The tail fin has a concave margin, with the tips prolonged into long dark brown filaments. The common triggerfish grows to a length of 12 inches. This member of the reef community may be found at times as far north as New York, drifting along in the Gulf Stream. The QUEEN TRIGGERFISH is more brilliantly colored and grows to a slightly larger size. This species is capable of rapid color changes, but the usual phase consists of a yellow body, blue and yellow fins, and blue

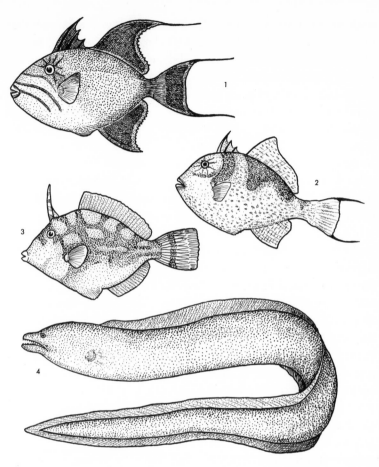

The unique Filefish Family includes queen triggerfish (1), common triggerfish (2), planehead filefish (3). The green moray (4) is a member of the Moray Eel Family. All figures adapted from Marineland (Florida) material.

bands across the head. The first rays of the dorsal fin, and the two outer tips of the tail fin are prolonged into tapering tips. The queen triggerfish shows a remarkable correlation between feeding habits and anatomy. The eyes are set far up on the head at some distance from the mouth. This enables the fish to catch crabs without having the waving claws damage its eyes. Competent observers have discovered that this triggerfish will not tackle crabs large enough for the claws to reach its eyes. Thus the fish limits the size of the crab it chooses to the distance between its own mouth and eyes.

Filefishes are so-named because of the hard rough skin, whose tough scales form a sandpaper-like surface. Some fishermen tack the filefish hide on the wall of their shack for use in striking matches. The PLANEHEAD FILEFISH, or common filefish, is a mottled slaty-gray fish capable of quick color changes. The young when feeding over marine meadows of green seaweed become a corresponding bright green protective color. The single erectile spine projects above the eyes like a horn. This filefish grows to a length of 10 inches; it is found as far north as Maine, as well as on the Florida reefs. More brilliantly colored is the ORANGE FILEFISH, of similar shape and general appearance. The orange-yellow body is speckled with irregular areas of small brown spots. An awkward fish, the orange filefish is often seen head-down browsing on the algae attached to wharf pilings. This is also a wide-ranging species, being found not only here among its tropical neighbors but also as far north as Maine.

Morays

The tropical paradise we have been exploring is not all color, beauty, and peace; it is also the home of several villainous species that prey on the many small fishes abundant in the coral gardens. Barracudas are ever present, ready to dart like an arrow at any reef fish that ventures too far from its craggy hiding place. Giant sharks prowl above casting their shadows over whole schools of sergeant majors or grunts. If we look closely into dark crevices, we may see a snake-like head projecting from a shadowy hiding place. This is the head of a moray. The Moray Family includes eels without either pectoral or pelvic fins (freshwater eels have pectoral fins). The thick leathery skin is entirely devoid of scales. A hundred species in this unprepossessing family inhabit the tropical Atlantic and Pacific oceans; ten species occur off our Atlantic Coast, one off the southern Pacific Coast. Morays are the largest of all eels and possess powerful jaws armed with vicious teeth. These marine carnivores hide amid rocks and coral, twining their long bodies into the crevices and striking like rattlesnakes at passing prey. Fishermen who hook one of these monsters prefer to cut the line rather than expose themselves to the thrashing body of their catch as it lashes about in the boat, capable of crunching a careless hand or foot.

The SPOTTED MORAY, an ever-present inhabitant of the coral reefs, is common from the West Indies to Florida. It reaches a length of 3 feet and has a mottled yellow and black body covered with small and large round spots. The coloring is an excellent camouflage as the moray hides among the coral grottoes. The back bears a long low dorsal fin along its ridge. The GREEN MORAY is a much larger and more ferocious eel attaining a length of 6 feet; it also is common among the Florida keys. Large specimens may weigh 25 pounds or more. Armed with sharp teeth, pugnacious and savage, this moray is a dangerous predator in the tropical paradise. It is usually brilliant grass green but may be slaty brown or mottled. The cause of this green color is rather unusual. If scraped off, the mucus coating of the skin is seen to be yellow while the skin beneath is bluish gray; the combination of the two results in the green color.

This is the colorful parade of fishes that we can view in any of the coral reef areas of the Florida waters. Our brief sojourn beneath the surface of the Key Largo Coral Preserve has revealed the many different ways in which nature has modified fishes to live amid particularly favorable surroundings. This environment is a far cry from the open sea, home of the silvery herring and the streamlined tuna; or from the rushing streams where trout and salmon live. But in each instance the fishes have become adapted for their own particular way of life, whether in the open sea, cold mountain streams, or in the warm sunny paradise of coral gardens.

When we surface and emerge into the bright, noisy above-water world, it seems as though we are suddenly propelled from one planet to another. For those fortunate enough actually to explore such an environment by aid of snorkels or aqualungs, an hour spent in our only underseas park will leave a lasting impression.

Strangest of all the fishes in the sea is the mammoth ocean sun-fish, reaching weights up to a ton; its huge body is all head, being abruptly cut off behind the dorsal and anal fins.

Marineland of Florida

Chapter Eight

Strange Creatures of the Sea

When we think of a fish, we usually picture a streamlined animal whose shape, body covering, and appendages are such that it can swim swiftly enough to capture its food or to escape its enemies. This is the "typical" fish that we encountered while exploring the lakes, rivers, and coastal waters of the United States. The tropical reef fishes, as we have just seen, have varied this pattern by adopting odd shapes to suit the life among coral and rocky habitats where streamlining and speed are not the chief essentials for survival. There are many other queerly formed and often grotesque species which roam the open seas or live in seclusion on the ocean bottom. The appearance and habits of these species are far different from those of our "typical" fish. Strange as some of their features may seem, they are usually special adaptations enabling the fishes to survive in the never-ending struggle to obtain food or foil their enemies. Many of these strange creatures of the sea occur in the waters off both our Atlantic and Pacific coasts.

One group has developed the effective protection of armor. This armor may consist of spiny scales, as in pufferfish and porcupine fish, or it may be a tortoiselike shell, as in the trunkfish and cowfish. Other groups have resorted to camouflage as protection and use trickery in capturing prey. Judged by human standards this is a weird assemblage of ugly, even repulsive species—as indicated by their common names of scorpion fish, batfish, frogfish, and toadfish. Others have equally picturesque names such as stargazer, sea robin, sargassum fish, and anglerfish. The snake-like cutlass fish and oarfish could well be the inspiration for sea serpent stories. To this collection of marine oddities can be added a number of fascinating individualists: the flying fish with its wing-like fins, the remora with its hitchhiking attachment, the ocean sunfish with its huge bulk, and the midget sea horses with their unusual habits.

Fishes in Armor

Throughout the animal kingdom we find species that have sacrificed speed for security. Protection by armor (see p. 50) was characteristic of the primitive fishes but, as bony fishes developed greater speed, protective armor was abandoned in exchange for agility. However, in a few families of otherwise modern fishes, armor is still relied upon as defense against enemies. Such are the puffer, porcupine fish, and trunkfish families.

The *Puffer Family* is represented by eight species on the Atlantic Coast, two on the Pacific. Puffers are clumsy, thickset fishes whose scales have become transformed into an armor of prickles. Puffers are able to swell their bodies to three times the normal size when frightened or handled. This they do by gulping water or air, and so inflating a saclike portion of the gullet through the functioning of special breathing valves. The increase in body size makes the prickles stick out like thorns on a cactus, resulting in an appearance that undoubtedly discourages predators. The NORTHERN PUFFER, found from Florida to New York, is a dusky brown fish with yellowish green or orange sides and a white belly; it grows to a length of 10 inches. This is an inshore species found over sandy bottoms where it searches for crustaceans and mollusks. A puffer can bury itself in the sand by using its collar bones as shovels, moving them easily beneath the loose baggy skin. Thus it lies hidden with only the eyes and top of the head visible.

The *Porcupine Fish Family* is related closely to the puffers; it includes five species on the Atlantic Coast and two on the Pacific. Like the puffers, porcupine fishes have very large fan-shaped pectoral fins, no ventral fins, a single small dorsal fin, and a small anal fin. The scales are modified into long sharp spines similar in appearance to porcupine quills; these can be folded close to the body and pointed backward when the fish is swimming. Porcupine fishes can also increase their size by gulping air or water. The COMMON PORCUPINE FISH is most abundant off the Florida coast, but individuals are sometimes found as far north as Massachusetts. It is a sandy or yellowish brown fish that grows to a length of 36 inches. When inflated it becomes a prickly balloon that can inflict painful wounds. Dried bodies of porcupine fishes are hollowed out and used as lanterns by the Japanese; by South Sea natives, as spiny helmets. The STRIPED BURRFISH, or spiny boxfish, is a cream-colored or yellowish green fish with irregular horizontal brown stripes and large dark brown spots. It is a smaller fish, usually less than 10 inches in length, with prominent spines along the back. This porcupine fish is a resident of the coral reef communities of Florida but at times ranges north to Cape Cod.

The *Trunkfish Family* has four members on the Atlantic Coast and one on the Pacific. These fishes have gone to an extreme in making use of armor, being encased entirely in a rigid shell made of fused scales. They are aquatic armored tanks able to move only their eyes and small fins. When viewed from the front, the body has a triangular outline, with the apex of the triangle at the top. With such rigid bodies, trunkfish swim sluggishly using only the fins for locomotion. Trunkfish exhibit a wide range of colors; some are

Spiny and armored fishes. The Puffer Family is represented by the northern puffer (1). The Trunkfish Family includes the cowfish (2) and common trunkfish (3). The prickly Porcupine Fish Family includes the common porcupine fish (4) and striped burrfish (5). Figure 1 adapted from Walter Chute in "Guide to the Shedd Aquarium"; 3 and 5 from Marineland (Florida) material; 4 from E. R. Sanborn photo in National Geographic Magazine.

vivid green, others are white, still others are brown. The COMMON TRUNKFISH of Florida grows to a length of 9 inches. A frequent color phase is a pearly gray background with dusky fins and a dark grayish band along the upper

sides. Young trunkfish a few inches in length are carried
north to Cape Cod by ocean currents in summer. The COW-
FISH, found from Florida to the Carolinas, is so-called because of the pair of hornlike spines, one over each eye. In
addition, three large spines on each side of the tail point
backward. Cowfish are yellowish with irregular blue horizontal stripes, yellow dorsal and anal fins. The small mouth
bears strong teeth capable of crushing the coral hiding places
of worms and other small invertebrates. Cowfish swim in a
slow stately fashion as they vibrate their small rudder-like
tail fin much as one sculls a boat with an oar. The pectoral
fins act as stabilizers keeping the cowfish from being propelled
forward as water is ejected from the gill opening. Cowfish
average 10 to 12 inches in length.

Camouflage and Trickery

Many of the fishes that live on the ocean bottom have
developed a variety of tubercles, spines, and fleshy outgrowths
that aid in camouflaging the fish amid rocks and marine vegetation. The coloring is also protective (see p. 50), imitating
that of the sandy or muddy environment. These camouflaged
bottom-dwellers belong to the Scorpion Fish, Sculpin, Frogfish, Batfish, and Toadfish Families. The names are suggestive
of their strange appearance. Some combine trickery with
camouflage: the Stargazer Family can deliver an electric
shock, the Anglerfish Family carries a built-in fishing rod for
catching its prey.

The *Scorpion Fish Family* is represented by over seventy
species found in both the Atlantic and Pacific oceans; the
family includes the numerous rockfishes. Scorpion fishes are
sedentary fishes with spiny heads, decorated with tentacles
of various sizes on head and chin. The spiny portion of the
dorsal fin is large, as are the wing-like pectoral fins. The
SPOTTED SCORPION FISH, a West Indies species that
ranges north into Florida waters, is a bewildering mixture

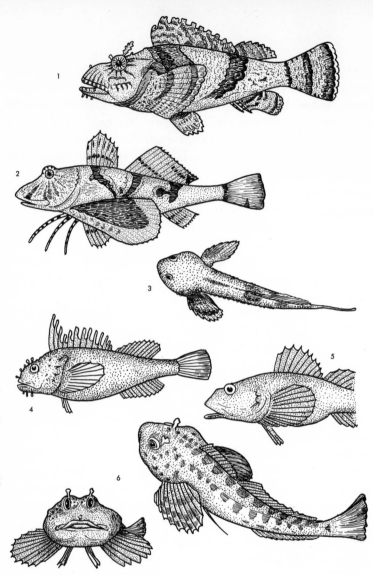

Camouflaged fishes. The Scorpion Fish Family is represented by the spotted scorpion fish (1). The Sea Robin Family includes the striped sea robin (2). The large Sculpin Family includes the freshwater sculpin (3), sea raven (4), shorthorn sculpin (5) and the cabezone (6). Figures 1 and 2 adapted from Marineland (Florida) material; 6 from Hashime Murayama in National Geographic Magazine.

of reds, greens, yellows, blues, and browns in no regular pattern. Against a coral reef background, such an attire is practically invisible as the fish rests motionless on the bottom. The common scorpion fish grows to a length of 12 inches. The LION-FISH is a smaller member of the family, only 8 inches in length. It is also a warm-water species, common in Florida, although individuals occasionally wander as far north as Maine. The lion-fish has a shaggy head because of many fleshy tabs and tubercles. A Polynesian relative of the lion-fish is armed with poisonous dorsal spines; each spine is grooved from tip to base, where a poison gland is located. The venom flows along the grooves in the spine into the wound made by the fin. Because of its poison, the fish is said to be as dangerous as a rattlesnake.

The *Sea Robin Family* is a large one, being represented by eighteen species in Atlantic waters and one in the Pacific Ocean. Sea robins have large grotesque heads and winglike pectoral fins; the latter feature accounts for their common name. Of the two dorsal fins, the forward one is very spiny; the ventral fins are located far forward beneath the head. The most distinctive feature consists of three fingerlike rays in front of each pectoral fin. These rays, hooked at the tip, are used in grasping stones and other objects on the sea bottom as the fish crawls about in search of mollusks and crustaceans. The NORTHERN SEA ROBIN, or common sea robin, is a brown or gray fish with darker saddles across the back and a yellowish white belly; it grows to a length of 16 inches. This species lives from low-tide mark to depths of 250 feet, from Florida to Cape Cod. The STRIPED SEA ROBIN, with the same general appearance, is a tan or brownish fish with spotted fins and striking brown-striped "fingers." It is a slightly smaller species, growing to a length of 12 inches, and is found along the south Atlantic and Gulf coasts.

The *Sculpin Family* is characterized by the same type of ungainly head and rapidly tapering body as in the sea robins. Sculpins also have similar wing-like pectoral fins, but these lack the fingerlike rays. The body is naked or armored with scales and prickles. This is a large family of cold-water fishes with over 80 species in American waters. Of these, 20 occur in freshwater habitats, fifty in the Pacific Ocean, and the remaining in the Atlantic. Sculpins are bottom-dwelling, repulsive fishes that are often caught on a hook—to the fisherman's disgust. The SEA RAVEN is a mottled reddish or purplish brown sculpin that grows to a maximum length of 25 inches and a weight of 7 pounds. Average individuals are 15 inches in length. Sea ravens are found at depths of less than three hundred feet from Maryland to northern New England. This unattractive fish is covered with tubercles and other outgrowths on the head and chin and is armed with long stiff spines on the forward dorsal fin and on the gill cover; the ventral fins are small and stiff-rayed. They are voracious eaters preying on a variety of aquatic invertebrates as well as fish, often tackling a fish larger than themselves. Another Atlantic Coast sculpin is the SHORTHORN SCULPIN common north of Cape Cod, with a brown back barred with black. Off the Pacific Coast from California northward lives a large sculpin, known as CABEZONE, that grows to a length of 30 inches and may weigh as much as 20 pounds. Its color varies with the surroundings, being greenish amid eelgrass and green seaweeds but brownish in kelp beds. This species, also known as blue cod or bullhead, is marketed on the west coast as a food fish. The SLIMY SCULPIN, or muddler, is one of the freshwater sculpins; it inhabits cold streams and lakes of eastern United States. As the name implies, it has a slimy coating. Unlike those of its saltwater relatives, the spines are only feebly developed. This sculpin spends most of the time hiding under stones; when venturing forth to feed on aquatic insects or algae, it is eaten by salmon and trout.

The *Frogfish Family* is represented in the United States by five eastern species and a single western one. Members of this family are awkward fishes only 3 to 6 inches in length, with the anterior portion of the body decorated with numerous appendages. The dorsal, anal, and tail fins are large; the pectoral and ventral fins resemble miniature limbs. Because of a wristlike joint at the base of the pectoral fin, frogfish can use these fins much as a land animal uses its forelimbs. SARGASSUM FISH is a common frogfish found in warm waters off our southeastern coast. As its name indicates, it lives amid the floating masses of brown seaweed known as sargassum. Sargassum fish has developed the art of camouflage to the point where the fish is practically indistinguishable from surrounding seaweeds. Its body and fins are mottled tan and brown, matching the colors of the sargassum. Numerous flat tabs and outgrowths of various sizes, some resembling individual "leaves" of the seaweed, clothe the head, chin, and body. Protected by this incredible mimicry, the tiny fish crawls frog-fashion through the seaweed pastures searching for a meal of small invertebrates.

The *Batfish Family* is another small but unusual family of fishes, with six species on the Atlantic Coast, one on the Pacific. They are flattened fishes of angular shape, with a triangular head that tapers into a pointed bony snout. Winglike pectoral fins, attached to the expanded sides of the body, have the same peculiar wrist joint as those of frogfishes. The COMMON BATFISH, about 9 inches in length, is a West Indies species common off Florida shores and occasionally found as far north as New York. It lives in shallow water, crawling over sandy bottoms by means of fleshy pectoral fins. Its toad-like appearance is accentuated by the warty skin.

Other unattractive but interesting fishes occur in the *Toadfish Family,* which includes four species in the Atlantic Ocean, two in the Pacific. These bottom-dwellers have flattened bodies, a forward dorsal fin reduced to a few spines, and a long low posterior dorsal fin. The toad-like head, covered with warty outgrowths, terminates in a large mouth with powerful jaws. The OYSTER TOADFISH, found from Virginia to Cape Cod, at times wanders as far north as Maine. It

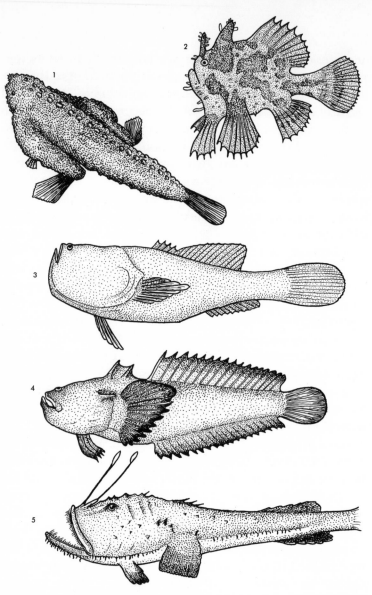

Oddities in the fish world. Batfish (1), sargassum fish (2), star-gazer (3), toadfish (4), anglerfish (5). Figure 2 adapted from Walter Chute, "Guide to the Shedd Aquarium"; 3 from C. M. Breder, "Field Book of Marine Fishes of the Atlantic Coast," 4 and 5 from L. P. Schultz, "Ways of Fishes."

is a squat, ugly fish growing to a length of 15 inches, protectively colored in mottled olive green or brown. The pectoral fins are broad and fan-like, the ventral fins are small and stiff and located beneath the head. Toadfishes live in shallow, weedy habitats where they hide beneath stones, darting out when hungry to catch crustaceans and mollusks.

Fishes in the *Stargazer Family* are so-named because of the upward-looking eyes. This family is represented by four species in the Atlantic, one in the Pacific Ocean. All are chunky fishes with mouth located on top of the head near the eyes; the forward portion of the dorsal fin bears a few short stout spines, and the pectoral fins are smaller and more pointed than those in the preceding families. Stargazers seem harmless, but they carry a unique electric weapon (see p. 52) on the head, undoubtedly useful in shocking an adversary or capturing prey. The NORTHERN STARGAZER is a dusky fish with irregular white spots on the upper side and dark blotches on the lower side; it grows to a length of 12 inches and is found on the ocean bottom from Virginia to New York. The stargazer often lies buried in sand waiting for a meal of small fishes or crustaceans, showing only its upturned eyes and protruding mouth.

In its depths, the sea hides many strange creatures, but none is so fantastic in appearance and habits as the anglerfish. It is the only species in the *Anglerfish Family* and found only in the Atlantic Ocean. The ANGLERFISH is common off our northeastern coast in summer, its range extending from Virginia to Maine. It is a far from beautiful fish. The head is broad and flattened, the enormous mouth lined with four rows of sharp inward-pointing teeth; the dwarfed body tapers rapidly to a small tail. A fringe of barbels hangs from the chin like a scraggly beard; other barbels extend in a line on either side of the body, some of them resembling bits of vegetation and so serving as camouflage. The entire fish is a mottled, chocolate brown color that harmonizes with the dingy tones of the ocean bottom. The base of the pectoral fin has a wristlike joint, as in the frogfishes and batfishes. When the anglerfish rests on the bottom, these fins look like deformed fleshy arms sprouting from the sides of the head. Anglerfish grow to a length of 4 feet and may weigh as much as 45 pounds. When hauled up by a fisherman expecting a cod or haddock, this grotesque catch causes understandable dismay. While other fish are content to lie passively on the bottom until prey come within reach, the anglerfish has adopted the technique of casting a baited line to attract the victim. It carries a built-in fishing rod on top of its head in the form of a slender spine thought to be a modified first ray of the dorsal fin. At its tip grows a baitlike lure. The anglerfish can move this fishing rod to and fro, dangling the lure to attract attention. As a curious fish rushes toward it, the lure is skillfully jerked out of the way. Eventually the rod is bent so that the lure dangles in front of the partly open mouth. As the victim darts for the lure, it heads into the anglerfish's mouth, which opens and shuts with a sudden snap, sucking the prey to its doom. By such trickery, the anglerfish catches cod, haddock, and other bottom-feeding fishes. The appetite of an anglerfish is astonishing; its taste unpredictable. It often comes to the surface and catches sea birds (hence another common name, goosefish); it has been known to swallow wooden lobster buoys, and one anglerfish was found near shore holding fast to a fox's leg!

Sea Serpents

Seafaring men have told many yarns of sea serpents encountered on their voyages. These have usually been ridiculed as tales recounted to add adventure to an experience. Yet many of the seamen may have been relating what they believed they actually saw. Two unusual fishes could be the basis of some sea serpent stories. These are the relatively rare cutlass fish and oarfish. Both are extremely elongated fishes that resemble serpents as they swim in undulating fashion near the surface of the sea.

The CUTLASS FISH belongs to the *Cutlass Fish Family* with two species in the Pacific and one in the Atlantic Ocean. It attains a length of 5 feet. The body is slender and eel-like with a long low dorsal fin; the pectoral fins are reduced in

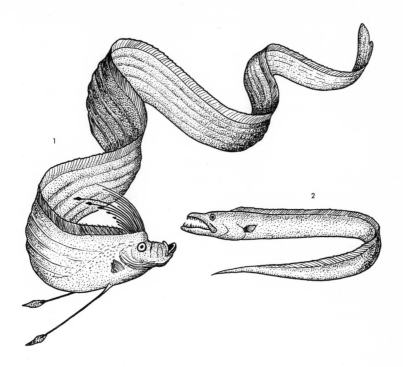

Sea serpents. Cutlass fish (2) and oarfish (1) could well be the cause of such stories. Figure 1 adapted from D. M. Blakeley in Natural History Magazine; 3 from C. M. Breder, "Field Book of Marine Fishes of the Atlantic Coast."

size, the ventral fins are lacking. It is a silvery fish living in warm waters; the eastern species can be found from the Gulf of Mexico to the Carolinas. Its name refers to the formidable array of many sharp, knifelike teeth in the large and powerful mouth. Few fishes, even the barracuda, have such terrifyingly armed jaws.

Much larger and rarer are the fishes in the *Oarfish Family,* which is represented by a little-known species in both the Atlantic and Pacific oceans. The name oarfish refers to the slender, long ventral spines that terminate in small oarlike blades. Other names for this unique fish is king-of-the-herrings, referring to the supposed habit of accompanying large schools of herring, and ribbonfish, because of the ribbonlike body. The OARFISH is an elusive fish; only a few naturalists have ever seen a living specimen. This rarity might account for its being mistaken for a sea serpent by an untrained observer. One oarfish encountered by a scientist in the south Pacific was 11 feet long, yet only 3 inches thick and about 12 inches deep. The blue and silvery body was adorned with a crest of scarlet dorsal spines 3 feet in length and ventral fins transformed into long slender streamers with oar-like tips. A smaller specimen was observed by another naturalist near Catalina Island, California. Its silvery body, frail as a ribbon, was marked by vivid zebralike stripes and carried the same scarlet crest and oarlike ventral appendages. A huge oarfish was hauled out of the southern California surf and killed by a fisherman who little realized the scientific importance of his find. The mutilated remains indicated a fish 21 feet long and estimated to weigh 600 pounds. This would make a respectably sized sea serpent.

Fishes and Flight

No fishes have accomplished true flight as have insects, bats, and birds. But several kinds of so-called "flying" fishes have taken to the air, soaring and gliding for several hundred yards before falling back into the water. They do this by using their enlarged and wing-like fins as gliding planes once they have attained sufficient speed to soar out of the water. Such a habit is thought to have originated as a means of escaping enemies in the water. Flying fishes belong to two families; Flying Fish Family and Flying Gurnard Family.

The *Flyingfish Family* is a large and successful one, with

over fifty species distributed through warm seas all over the world; eleven species occur in our Atlantic waters, three in the Pacific. The body of a flying fish has a blunt nose and

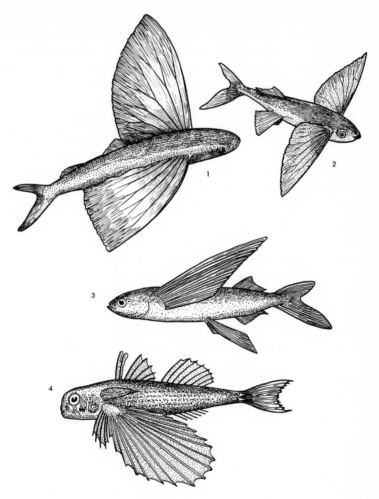

Fishes that have attempted to soar in the air include the various species of flying fishes (1, 2, 3) and the flying gurnard (4). Figure 1 adapted from Harold Edgerton photo in National Geographic Magazine; 2 and 4 from L. P. Schultz, "The Ways of Fishes."

bears a single dorsal fin. The tail fin is lobed unequally, the larger lower lobe being effective in propelling the fish along the surface water until it becomes air-borne. The main support in the air comes from the extremely large, often semi-transparent, pectoral fins that extend outward from the anterior part of the fish like airplane wings. In some species the ventral fins are also enlarged and act as airfoils. As a flying fish taxis over the water, the body becomes raised at an angle from the force of the tail's propulsion; the fins do not move and so the resulting flight is a gliding maneuver consisting of a series of hops over the water. Flying fishes have difficulty rising into the air on a calm day, as taking off into a wind makes it easier to become air-borne. The spectacular glides are usually prompted by pursuit by the flying fish's arch enemies, the bonito and the dolphin. The ATLANTIC FLYING FISH is a bluish gray fish with silvery sides, reaching a length of 15 inches. It is commonly seen in the Gulf Stream from Florida north to Cape Cod. This is the familiar flying fish encountered by boats in the mid-Atlantic region. The CALIFORNIA FLYING FISH, 12 to 18 inches in length, occurs in great numbers off Catalina Island; it has the same coloring and general appearance.

The *Flying Gurnard Family,* with a single American species found off our southeastern coast, is closely related to the sea robins. FLYING GURNARD is an olive-green or brown fish 12 inches in length with a hard bony head and frog-like mouth and eyes. The pectoral fins, as in the flying fish, are enlarged and serve as wings when the fish soars into the air. The ventral fins are stiff and directed downward, useful to the gurnard when it walks along the bottom. Another specialization is the transformation of the first three rays of the pectoral fins into feelers used in searching for food. When removed from water, the flying gurnard makes a peculiar grunting noise by vibrating a partition that extends across the cavity of its air bladder.

Hitchhikers of the Sea

Man is not the only organism that has discovered that the easiest way to get from one place to another is to obtain a free ride. Fishes have done this by developing a means of attachment to another animal. Such an ingenious device exists among the fishes in the *Remora Family,* with over half a dozen species common to both our Atlantic and Pacific waters.

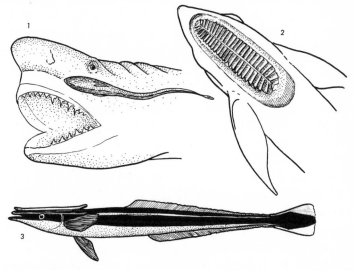

Hitchhikers of the sea. Remora (1) attached to a shark; sucker disk of a remora (2); streamlined profile of a remora (3). Figures 1 and 2 adapted from Natural History Magazine; 3 from Marine- land (Florida) material.

Fishes in this family have the typical streamlined body of an ordinary fish. Although capable of swimming swiftly by themselves, they prefer to travel the effortless way: attached to the body of a larger fish. This is accomplished by a unique sucker- disk considered to be a modified dorsal fin and located on the top of the head. The disk consists of a series of cross-partitions that can open and shut like the slats of a shutter. When a remora comes in contact with a larger fish—commonly a shark or swordfish—the shutters open and create a vacuum that holds the remora fast to its carrier. Remoras are not parasites and do not harm their obliging carriers; they feed on the fragments of food discarded or overlooked by the larger predator. The ATLANTIC REMORA, also known as shark-sucker, is a slaty brown or gray fish with a conspicuous broad, dark stripe along its side. The long slim body bears a reduced dorsal and anal fin and small pectoral and ventral fins. The remora reaches a length of 3 feet yet weighs less than 2 pounds; it inhabits the warm waters off our southeastern coast but occurs at times as far north as Cape Cod.

A Genial Giant

The largest bony fish in the sea is a harmless giant, the OCEAN SUNFISH, member of the *Ocean Sunfish Family*, with three American species found in both the Atlantic and Pacific oceans. This mammoth fish lives in the open ocean but occasionally becomes stranded on a beach or is harpooned as a curiosity. It is an absurd-looking fish seeming to be all head and no body and covered with a thick leathery skin. The truncated posterior suggests that the rest of the fish was chopped off behind the tall dorsal and anal fins. The body is circular in outline; it is dusky gray on the back, silvery gray on the sides, and white on the belly. The giant gets its name from a habit of basking near the surface. Average individuals measure 4 feet deep, but a record California specimen was 11 feet in diameter and weighed a ton! In spite of its size, the ocean sunfish feeds on tiny aquatic organisms such as crustaceans and jellyfish. It has long puzzled naturalists to explain how a fish of such huge proportions can find enough of this minute food to maintain its bulk.

Sea Horses and Their Kin

In shifting our attention from the giant sunfish to those fascinating midgets, the sea horses and their relatives, we go

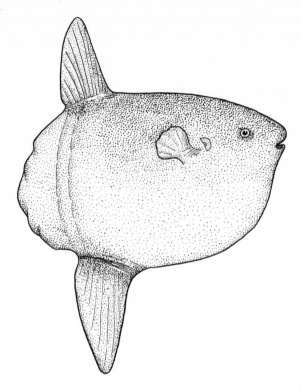

The ocean sunfish is a genial giant of the sea. Adapted from L. P. Schultz, "The Ways of Fishes."

from one extreme to the other. The *Pipefish Family,* with about two dozen species, found in both the Atlantic and Pacific oceans, includes the sea horse as well as pipefish. In this family, the body is armored with small plates instead of being clothed in scales; the long snout terminates in a small sucking mouth, and the gill opening is reduced to a small pore. The family is noted for its unusual reproductive habits (see p. 60). In the pipefishes the lengthwise axis of the body continues through the head, whereas in the sea horses the head is at right angles to the rest of the body. Pipefishes have a normal tail terminated by a tail fin, but in sea horses there is no tail fin and the tail is used to grasp objects.

The NORTHERN PIPEFISH, found along the Atlantic Coast from Virginia to New England, is a slender fish that grows to a length of 12 inches. It is green, brown, or reddish in color depending upon its surroundings. This pipefish lives among seaweeds and on sandy bottoms in brackish or salt water where it feeds on small crustaceans. The DUSKY PIPE-FISH is a slightly smaller species with brown speckled sides and silvery belly, and found from Virginia southward along the Atlantic Coast. On the Pacific Coast from California to Alaska lives the BAY PIPEFISH, which grows to a length of 12 inches. It changes so rapidly from green to brown that this species is another "chameleon of the sea."

Few fishes can compare with the diminutive sea horse in its

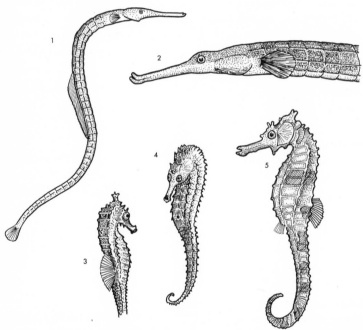

The Pipefish Family includes northern pipefish (1, 2), and the spotted sea horse (3, 4, 5). Figure 1 adapted from L. P. Schultz, "The Ways of Fishes"; figures 3, 4, 5 from William Beebe in Natural History Magazine.

appeal. The SPOTTED SEA HORSE, common in Florida waters and in summer ranging northward to Cape Cod, exhibits different color phases according to the amount of light in its environment. Sometimes it is gray, at other times greenish or brown, at still other times silvery black. This sea horse averages 5 or 6 inches in length. Other species are smaller. But all sea horses are of similar appearance and habits. The sea horse is confined in a strait jacket of armored rings with flattened sides, extending from head to tail. The arched head bears an uncanny resemblance to the head of a horse; the eyes can move independently of each other, as those of a chameleon, aiding the sea horse in its keen vision. The tube-like mouth opens and closes with an audible smack creating a suction that sweeps in the small shrimps that constitute its chief diet. Sea horses swim in a vertical position, moved by the whirling of the tiny dorsal fin. The small pectoral fins are used mainly to maintain equilibrium in the vertical position. Sea horses ascend by straightening the body, descend by arching the head and curling the tail inward. The tail is not used in swimming but, being as prehensile as the tail of a monkey, is used to anchor the sea horse to a bit of seaweed or to creep along the bottom. Its appealing habits make the sea horse a fascinating aquarium fish, but unfortunately few amateurs can keep it alive. Sea horses require a constant supply of live shrimps as food and must be kept in salt water.

The cartilaginous fishes include the huge and often voracious sharks. This shark is giving a free ride to a remora, or shark sucker, attached to its lower surface. Marineland of Florida

Chapter Nine

The Cartilaginous Fishes

All the fishes we have encountered thus far have had one feature in common: a skeleton of bone. In this they are like the land vertebrates—the amphibians, reptiles, birds, and mammals. But some fishes lack a bony skeleton and have instead a skeleton of cartilage. The best known of these cartilaginous fishes are lampreys, sharks, and rays. Another characteristic of these fishes is the type of gill opening. In the bony fishes there is a single large gill opening on each side of the head, protected by a gill cover. In the lampreys and sharks the gill openings are a series of round or slitlike apertures along the side of the head. The lampreys have sucker-mouths instead of mouths with movable jaws and lack paired fins. The sharks and rays, on the other hand, have hinged jaws and paired fins.

The Lampreys

The *Lamprey Family* is represented by fourteen species in American waters. Of these, ten live in fresh water, the others live in the sea but migrate, like salmon, into freshwater habitats to spawn. Lampreys occur on both the Atlantic and Pacific coasts. A lamprey is an elongated and cylindrical fish with small rounded head, beady eyes, and a circular mouth studded with conical teeth. The opening into the small throat reveals a rough tongue with rasping teeth on its surface. The dorsal fin is long and low, extending to the tail fin; the body is smooth and scaleless. On each side of the head is a row of seven small "portholes" that are the gill openings. Although

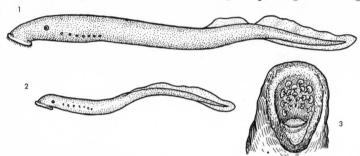

The Lamprey Family includes such eel-like fishes as the sea lamprey (1) and brook lamprey (2). The jawless mouth of a lamprey (3) is armed with many conical teeth.

the lamprey is often mistaken for an eel and sometimes called lamprey-eel, its sucker-mouth and lack of pectoral fins are distinctive differences. Some species, such as the brook lamprey, spend all their lives in freshwater streams and ponds; they are nonparasitic and harmless. The sea lamprey lives in the ocean but migrates into streams to spawn in spring.

The SEA LAMPREY is a mottled brownish or greenish fish reaching a length of 3 feet and a weight of several pounds. An eastern species is common from Maine to Florida; two additional species occur along the Pacific Coast. The sea lamprey attaches itself to the body of a larger fish by means of its sucker-mouth. The horny tongue rasps through the flesh enabling the lamprey to feed on the blood of the unfortunate host. When mature, sea lampreys migrate up coastal streams to spawn; the run takes place chiefly at night during May and June. Males and females cooperate in selecting a site, usually in shallow, swift-flowing water over a gravelly or pebbly bottom. They construct a crude nest by clearing a depression some six inches deep and several feet in diameter, removing stones with their mouths. Each female deposits in the nest about 200,000 eggs, which hatch without any special parental care. The young fish are born toothless and blind; they are called ammocoetes. Hiding in the bottom sediments for several years, they feed on minute aquatic organisms. At the end of the larval period they reach a length of 6 inches. A metamorphosis then takes place, the ammocoete developing eyes and mouth and otherwise becoming like the adult. They are now ready for the return trip to the sea. The entire life cycle lasts five to eight years.

In some cases, a lamprey population becomes landlocked and never returns to the sea; this has happened in the Great Lakes. After the Welland Canal was built, sea lampreys were able to bypass Niagara Falls and thus invade the upper Great Lakes. These lampreys found the new feeding grounds much to their liking, and an incredible population increase suddenly took place. Millions upon millions of lampreys so effectively parasitized the native whitefish, lake trout, and other valuable food species that these fishes have become almost extinct. Lampreys became established in Lake Huron in the late 1930's. The annual catch of lake trout was then about one million pounds; the devastating toll brought about by the lampreys reduced the catch to less than a hundred pounds in 1951. The sea lamprey moved on into Lake Michigan, and the carnage was repeated. In 1945 the lake trout catch there was over five million pounds, but ten years later it was reduced to four hundred pounds. Now the lampreys are moving on into Lake Superior, and science is marshaling all its knowhow to stem the advance and prevent a repetition of the destruction. Techniques have been developed to destroy the larvae in the streams by chemicals and to trap the spawning individuals as they travel up the streams. But the battle is not yet won.

Table 7. Giants Among the Cartilaginous Fishes

Species	Weight (in pounds)	Length (in feet)
Whale Shark	26,000 (est.)	38
Basking Shark	8,600	30
Manta	3,500	20 (width)
White Shark	2,664	17
Greenland Shark	2,250 (est.)	21
Tiger Shark	1,422	13
Mako Shark	1,000	12
Thresher Shark	922	16 (est.)
Hammerhead Shark	900	13
Sawfish	736	16
Nurse Shark	370	8
Northern Stingray	350 (est.)	7
Sand Shark	250	9
Torpedo	200 (est.)	6

The Sharks

A group of animals often includes some species about which popular ideas are inaccurate. In the fish world, this is the fate of the sharks. The cry of "shark" along a bathing beach is guaranteed to create consternation and even hysteria. It is true that many sharks are voracious predators, but their man-eating propensities have been greatly exaggerated. In spite of the huge size of many species and their hideous array of sharp teeth, most sharks are timid, wary fishes preferring to attack smaller defenseless animals and to avoid any prey that might put up a fight. In fact, the odds of being attacked by a shark along our shores are about the same as being struck by lightning—certainly far less than of being injured in an automobile accident. Some years ago a reward of 500 dollars was offered in New York City newspapers for authentic evidence of a shark attack on a human being, but the reward was never claimed. Actual fatalities are few. It is true that in tropical seas sharks are a greater menace. But even in the tropics shark attacks are most common at night and in deep offshore waters rather than along the beaches. On a world-wide scale, their depredations on humans are not great; most occur in Australian and Polynesian waters. The most danger-ous species—the white shark, mako shark, and tiger shark—are uncommon near our shores. The cry of "shark" when a high dorsal fin is seen cleaving the water is usually caused by the sight of the fin of either a harmless shark or a swordfish.

Some sharks reach a tremendous size; in fact the largest living fish (see p. 23) is the whale shark, whose bulk is meas-ured in tons rather than pounds. Sharks can be proud of their genealogy, for they represent the oldest vertebrates. In fact some of their ancestors were even larger than today's species and were as unquestioned "lords of the sea" then as now. For several hundred millions of years they have dominated the seas. They occur today throughout the world, being as much at home under Arctic ice as cruising over coral reefs. Their commercial importance as a food or sport fish is only minor; more valuable is the liver oil used medicinally and indus-trially. The durable hide of some species is made into leather goods, while some sharks are processed into livestock and poultry feed.

A typical shark has a long lithe body which is broadest behind the head and tapers to a tail bearing a large tail fin. Sharks swim by wave contractions that pass along each side of the body and give the shark a sinuous movement unlike that of other fishes. The pointed conical head has an overshot upper jaw so that the mouth is on the lower side. The body is well protected by a tough hide that in some species, such as the whale shark, may be four inches thick and practically impenetrable. The rough skin is covered with many small placoid scales. A shark has two dorsal fins, the forward one being very large and cutting the water when the fish swims near the surface. The gill openings consist of five or more slits along the side of the head.

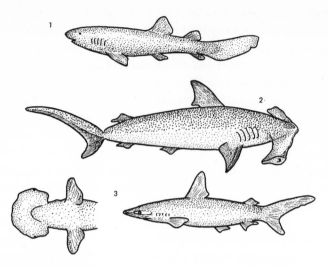

The Nurse Shark Family is represented by the harmless nurse shark (1). The Hammerhead Shark Family includes the smooth hammerhead (2) and the bonnethead (3). Figure 2 adapted from Francesca La Monte, "North American Game Fishes." Figures 1 and 3 from C. M. Breder, "Field Book of Marine Fishes of the Atlantic Coast."

Although the body of a shark is sleek and supple, it is difficult to think of the large toothy mouth in any other terms than "hideous" or "terrifying." Most sharks are inveterate cannibals, feeding upon their own kind as well as on all other fishes, sea turtles, sea lions, and seals. Many sharks are also scavengers and eat refuse thrown from ships. Eating motivates the entire life of a shark; it is constantly on the lookout for a meal, and the presence of fresh blood will send it into a frenzy. A common misconception is that sharks have to turn over to catch their prey. Sharks frequently move in a rolling motion, but this is only to get a better view of their surroundings because the eyes on top of the head give little forward or downward vision. Sharks lack an air bladder; thus they must regulate their depth by swimming, one reason that sharks are constantly on the move.

American sharks belong to eight families, each with its own distinctive features. These include differences in the shape of the head, location of the dorsal fins, and type of tail fin. The *Hammerhead Shark Family* is unusual in having the head expanded on each side, which gives the forward end of the shark a T-shaped outline when viewed from above. This family includes the common hammerhead shark and the bonnethead shark. All the other families have conical or pointed heads. The *Nurse Shark Family* can be recognized by the position of the first dorsal fin, which is located practically above the ventral fin. In other sharks, the first dorsal fin is located farther forward in front of the ventral fins. The shape of the tail fin is important in distinguishing the remaining families. In two families the tail is strengthened by a keel on either side, and the nearly symmetrical tail fin has a crescent-shaped margin. This is distinctive of the *Whale Shark Family* and the *Mackerel Shark Family;* the latter includes the porbeagle, bonito, white, mako, and basking sharks. In all the other families the tail fin is not symmetrical, the upper lobe being much larger than the lower lobe. This is a distinguishing feature of the *Sand Shark Family;* the *Thresher Shark Family;* the *Requiem Family,* which includes the sandbar, tiger, leopard, and smooth dogfish sharks; and the *Dogfish Shark Family,* comprising the spiny dogfish and the Greenland shark.

The SMOOTH HAMMERHEAD SHARK is a grayish or brownish shark with a blunt head that extends laterally into fleshy projections. These grotesque appendages may serve as a bow rudder aiding this fast-swimming shark to maneuver quickly as it pursues its prey. It is also thought that the expanded head may be of use in detecting food, as the nasal groove extends along its entire forward edge. Hammerhead sharks do have an unusually keen sense of smell, being able to pick up a scent from a great distance. The eyes are located on the outer tip of the appendages. Hammerheads are large sharks growing to a length of 17 feet; a 13-foot individual weighs 900 pounds. This species inhabits warm and temperate seas throughout the world; off our eastern coast it is found from Florida to New York, and in the West, off southern California. It roams the open seas in search of smaller fishes and squid. In summer, large schools of hammerheads often appear off the New Jersey–New York coast where they are frequently caught by fishermen.

The NURSE SHARK is a harmless brown or gray shark with a distinctive pair of barbels on either side of the mouth; the first dorsal fin is set far back above the ventral fins. Nurse sharks reach a length of 14 feet but most individuals are half that size. This shark is a sluggish, warm-water species common off the Atlantic Coast from Florida to the Carolinas. It cruises close to shore, frequently being seen in the shallow water near sandy beaches. The sight of its dorsal fin rising high about the water undoubtedly is a frequent cause of shark scares. Nurse sharks feed on crustaceans, squid, and refuse.

A symmetrical, or nearly symmetrical, tail fin with a crescent-shaped margin is characteristic of the whale shark and mackerel shark families. In the mackerel sharks, the body contour and tail fin design is typical of fast-swimming fishes. The PORBEAGLE, or common mackerel shark, is a gracefully proportioned shark with a blue-gray body and a high dorsal fin situated far forward just behind the pectoral fins. It has a conspicuous keel on either side of the tail. The porbeagle is an Atlantic species that roams the open seas preying on schools of mackerel and herring. It is common north of Cape Cod. Porbeagles are often found basking at the surface far from shore, with the dorsal fin projecting above the water. They are medium-sized, harmless sharks, ordinarily 4 to 5 feet in length. A large porbeagle caught off the English coast was 8 feet long and weighed 271 pounds. The BONITO SHARK, of similar appearance and habits, occurs in California coastal waters; it grows to a length of 20 feet. The MAKO SHARK, or sharp-nosed mackerel shark, is a dark blue-gray species found off the Atlantic Coast from Florida

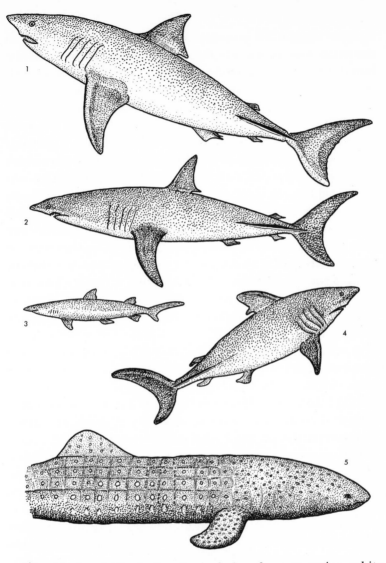

The Mackerel Shark Family includes the man-eating white shark (1), the mako shark (2), and the porbeagle (4). Other families include the sand shark (3) and the whale shark (5). Figures 1, 2, and 4 adapted from Francesca La Monte, "North American Game Fishes." Figure 3 adapted from C. H. Breder, "Field Book of Marine Fishes of the Atlantic Coast." 5 adapted from photo by Schaper Brothers in Natural History Magazine.

to New England. It is a medium-sized shark very similar to the porbeagle except for minor anatomical features. Large individuals reach a length of 12 feet and weigh up to 1000 pounds. Mako sharks are fast swimmers, usually found offshore where they can prey on herring, mackerel, and swordfish.

The WHITE SHARK is also known as the man-eater shark. Except for its greater size and strength, it is very similar to the porbeagle. This ashy gray or leaden white shark is a heavyweight with the added traits of great speed and voraciousness. A 21-foot specimen weighs over 7000 pounds. The white shark is undoubtedly one of the most powerful and dangerous of living fishes and one of the few species with an authentic record of attacking human beings. It occurs off the Florida coast; being a fish of warm waters, it rarely ventures as far northward as New England. On the west coast, it is found north to Monterey, California. World-wide in distribution, its customary haunts are the open seas, but occasionally it comes inshore to the shallow water off beaches. Its normal diet consists of large fishes such as tuna, and of sea turtles, seals, and sea lions.

The BASKING SHARK, closely related to the preceding species, differs in having extremely long gill slits that almost meet under the throat. It possesses very small teeth, a peculiarity that makes it necessary for this shark to be a filter-feeder. Thus it spends most of the time swimming through the seas with mouth open to collect minute plankton that is sifted from the incoming water by gill rakers. Basking sharks vary in color from brown and gray to black; in size they rate as second largest of all fishes, being outclassed only by the whale sharks. A 30-foot basking shark weighs over 4 tons. The basking shark has a circumpolar distribution in both the northern Atlantic and Pacific oceans. Formerly it was common as far south along the Atlantic Coast as Cape Cod, but its numbers were diminished in the oil-lamp era because of its value as a source of liver oil, a vital fuel of that age.

The largest living fish is the WHALE SHARK, a harmless

and inoffensive giant with authenticated lengths of over 30 feet and weights well in excess of 12 tons! Whale sharks are a relatively rare species of which little is known. They live in tropical waters of both the Atlantic and Pacific oceans. Eight specimens of this leviathan of the deep have been recorded in Florida, and one—the farthest north ever recorded—became ensnared in a fisherman's net near Fire Island, New York. A whale shark is reddish or greenish brown, decorated with a bizarre checkerboard pattern made of crisscrossing white and yellowish lines. In some individuals the center of each square has a bright yellow spot. The huge size of this shark can be imagined when one realizes that the Fire Island specimen had a tail fin with a spread of 9 feet, a head 5 feet wide with a yard-wide mouth, and a dorsal fin 2 feet tall. Since whale sharks are equipped with very small teeth, only one-eighth inch in length, they cannot prey on large fish but are restricted to plankton and other small aquatic organisms that they obtain in the manner of all filter-feeders.

All the remaining sharks can be recognized by very unsymmetrical tail fins, usually with a greatly enlarged upper lobe. Of these, the most abundant is the SAND SHARK of the Atlantic Coast occurring from Virginia to Cape Cod. This harmless shark, brown or mottled in color, is generally about 5 feet in length; a record individual 9 feet long weighed 250 pounds. Like other sharks with similar tail fins, the dorsal fin is situated midway along the back; the upper lobe of the tail fin is several times the size of the lower lobe. Young sand sharks often have yellowish brown spots along the sides of the body and on the dorsal and tail fins. Sand sharks are sluggish fish—feeding on smaller aquatic animals in the shallow water off beaches; they are frequently caught by surfcasters fishing for other species.

The numerous species in the *Requiem Shark Family* can be recognized by the two dorsal fins, the anterior dorsal in front of the ventral fins, the second dorsal smaller and above the anal fin, and by the unequally lobed tail fin. This family includes most of the common sharks seen near bathing

The thresher shark has a huge unsymmetrical tail fin (1). The Requiem Shark Family includes the smooth dogfish shark (2), tiger shark (3), and leopard shark (4). The spiny dogfish (5) is a member of the Dogfish Shark Family. Figure 1 adapted from American Museum of Natural History photo; 2 from C. M. Breder, "Field Book of Marine Fishes of the Atlantic Coast"; 3 from Francesca La Monte, "North American Game Fishes"; 4 from Hashime Murayama in National Geographic Magazine.

beaches. It is doubtful if any of this family ever has attacked a swimmer. The SANDBAR SHARK, also known as the brown shark or New York ground shark, is a medium-sized species attaining a length of 8 feet and a weight of 200 pounds. Sandbar sharks are brownish with a lighter underside; they are often found in the shallow water over sandbars in bays and harbors. They range along the Atlantic Coast from Florida to New England; in summer they are often caught by fishermen off New Jersey and New York. Sandbar sharks feed on flounders, crustaceans, and mollusks.

The LEOPARD SHARK is another relatively small shark, found along the Pacific Coast north to San Francisco. This harmless shark is gray in color with saddlelike crossbars on the back and spots along the sides. It is usually less than 5 feet in length. The leopard shark is the most common shark in California waters. Its flesh is considered very tasty and is sold in the markets of California, as it is also in Europe. The skin of the leopard shark is used in making leather goods.

The smallest of the common sharks is the harmless SMOOTH DOGFISH SHARK, a slaty gray species with yellowish underside, usually only 2 or 3 feet in length. It is found in harbors and bays along the entire Atlantic Coast north to Cape Cod and is considered a nuisance by fishermen. It is an omnivorous feeder, thriving as well on refuse as on lobsters and other crustaceans.

Largest member of the family is the TIGER SHARK, a grayish or brown shark found throughout the world in tropical and subtropical waters. On the Atlantic Coast it occurs only off southern Florida but on the Pacific is found along the entire California–Oregon coast. Young individuals are conspicuously striped with vertical dark bars along the sides. A 13-foot specimen caught off the coast of Australia weighed over 1300 pounds. Tiger sharks have a goat-like appetite, feeding on a variety of fishes and invertebrates as well as on all kinds of refuse thrown from ships.

The THRESHER SHARK, found in both the Pacific and

Atlantic oceans, is equipped with the hugest and most un-symmetrical tail of all the sharks. The mammoth upper lobe is often as long as the rest of the shark's body. A thresher shark is brownish or bluish gray with a mottled or white underside. It is an inhabitant of temperate seas, occurring as far north as New York on the Atlantic Coast and north to Oregon on the Pacific Coast. An average individual is 15 feet in length and weighs over 500 pounds. Thresher sharks are usually en-countered a few miles offshore roaming near the surface after such schooling fishes as mackerel, menhaden, and herring. They swim about a school in narrowing circles, using the flail-like tail to herd the prey into a compact mass prior to the kill.

The SPINY DOGFISH SHARK is a small, common shark that can be recognized by the absence of an anal fin and by a sharp spine in front of each dorsal fin. This is a cold-water species of both the Atlantic and Pacific oceans; on the Atlantic Coast it occurs from Virginia northward. Average individuals are 3 to 4 feet in length and weigh under 20 pounds. The spiny dogfish, a slaty gray fish with lighter underparts, might be confused with the smooth dogfish shark except for the spines and the lack of an anal fin. Spiny dog-fish are sluggish feeders traveling in schools as they search for worms, jellyfishes, squids, and small fishes. They use the dorsal spines for defense, curling up in a bow-like position and then

Skates, rays, and mantas are relatives of the sharks: cow-nosed ray (1), California electric ray (2), little skate (4), stingray (5), manta (6). The unique sawfish (3) is also a relative of the sharks. Figure 1 adapted from Marineland (Florida) photo; 2 from Hashime Murayama in National Geographic Magazine; 3 from L. P. Schultz, "The Ways of Fishes"; 4 from C. M. Breder, "Field Book of Marine Fishes of the Atlantic Coast"; 5 and 6 from Francesca La Monte, "North American Game Fishes."

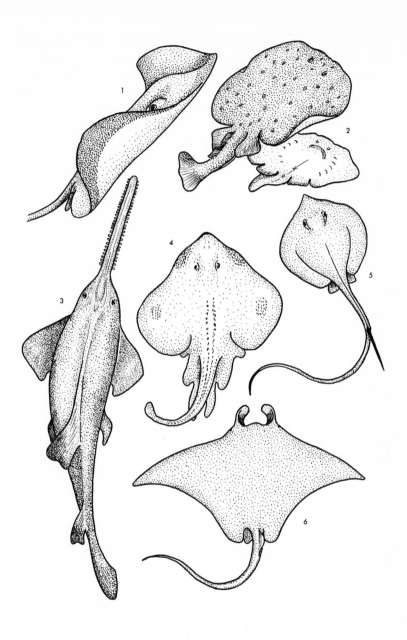

striking at the attacker. Canned spiny dogfish is sold as "gray-fish"; in Europe the freshly caught fish is sold in the markets. The GREENLAND SHARK is related to the spiny dogfish but is a much larger species; it is also an inhabitant of cold arctic waters but at times wanders as far south as Cape Cod. The entire body is one color, usually dark brown or grayish black. Individuals reach a length of 20 feet and may weigh up to a ton. In spite of its size the Greenland shark is harmless and sluggish, living most of the time on the ocean bottom where it feeds on cod, halibut, and haddock.

The Rays and Skates

The American rays and skates make up a large group of over fifty species, belonging to a half a dozen families. They are actually sharks with flattened bodies adapted to a bottom-dwelling existence. The broad pectoral fins are fused with the body to form a disk often as wide as long, with a wing-like appearance—a resemblance that is furthered by their graceful undulations as the fish "fly" through the water. Rays and skates can be separated into two groups on the basis of the shape of the tail and the number of dorsal fins. One group has a thick spineless tail with two dorsal fins. This includes the *Skate Family,* with representatives on both the Atlantic and Pacific coasts, and the *Torpedo Family,* with species also on both coasts. The other group has a slender whiplike tail, usually with one or two long spines and either a single dorsal fin or none at all. The two families in this group occur on both the Atlantic and Pacific coasts. They are the *Stingray Family,* represented by eleven American species, and the *Manta Family,* consisting of three species.

The tail of a skate is slender and muscular with a longitudinal fold of skin on either side. Viewed from above, it has a broadly triangular outline and a small snout. Since the eyes are close together in the middle of the top of the head, a skate can lie partly buried in the bottom mud or sand, safe from enemies and yet be able to lie in wait for prey. Their grayish or brown colors are excellent camouflage. In Europe, the pectoral fins of the skate are considered a delicacy.

The LITTLE SKATE, or common skate, is an eastern species living in shallow water from the Carolinas to New England. The upper surface of the smooth-skinned body is spotted with dark brown, the lower surface is white or gray. This is a small skate, ordinarily under 2 feet in length and weighing less than 2 pounds. It is the most common skate of the mid-Atlantic Coast where it haunts shallow inshore waters for its diet of crustaceans, mollusks, and small fishes. The CLEARNOSE SKATE, or brier skate, is of the same coloring and shape but differs in having a row of spines along the back and translucent areas on either side of the snout. This is a larger skate, reaching a length of 31 inches and weighing up to 6 pounds and found in shallow water from Florida to Massachusetts. It is often caught by surfcasters off the mid-Atlantic beaches. Largest is the BARN-DOOR SKATE with smoother skin than the clearnose skate but similar dark brown spotted coloring. It attains a length of 6 feet and a weight of 40 pounds. The barn-door skate is found in offshore waters from Florida to Maine where it feeds on crabs, lobsters, squids, and smaller fishes, and is often caught by "deep sea" fishing parties. Barn-door skates make up most of the commercial skate catch of the Atlantic states.

The ATLANTIC TORPEDO, or electric ray, is a ray with a short thick tail and a small tail fin; two small dorsal fins are located in front of the tail. Unlike the skates, which have a small pointed snout, the torpedo has a rounded outline to the head. It is a chocolate-brown or purplish gray fish, well camouflaged when it lies partly buried in mud or sand. It reaches a length of 5 feet and may weigh as much as 75 pounds; the average individual, however, is much smaller. The torpedo is common in water from 60 to 300 feet deep, and although its range is from Florida to Maine, it is rare north of Cape Cod. This ray is unique (see p. 53) in its possession of electric organs on its head. Like the sharks, torpedoes give birth to living young.

The stingrays are skatelike fishes with a triangular outline when viewed from above, the body sometimes being even greater in width than in length. The distinctive feature is a large spine with a saw-toothed edge located on the top of the whiplike tail. This is an effective means of defense, even against man. Stingrays have strong crushing teeth suited to a diet of mollusks and crustaceans. This ray gives birth to living young, as do the torpedoes and sharks. The ROUGH-TAIL STINGRAY, or northern stingray, is an olive-brown ray white on the undersurface, with a long slender tail. It is the largest stingray of the Atlantic Coast with a reported maximum length of 7 feet and weight of 350 pounds. This stingray is found in the shoal waters of inlets and bays from Virginia to Maine; it is frequently caught by fishermen off the New Jersey–New York beaches. Numerous species of similar appearance and habits live off the Pacific Coast, among them the BUTTERFLY RAY and the ROUND STINGRAY.

The ATLANTIC MANTA, or devilfish, common off our southeastern coast, is a bat-like ray that grows to a width of 20 feet and may weigh as much as 3000 pounds. The huge pectoral fins are expanded to form undulating "wings," and an additional set of fleshy outgrowths known as cephalic fins form a pair of "horns" on either side of the snout. The body, covered with tiny tubercles, is dark brown or black in color and contrasting white on the underside. The corners of the pectoral fins are pointed like the wings of a bird; the cephalic fins form a scoop that funnels prey into the huge mouth. These lobes, made up of leathery muscle tissue, resemble animated horns as the manta swims gracefully through the water. They close automatically when any object touches the portion of the head between them. Mantas have been reported to cause the death of divers by clamping the cephalic fins around the air hose; mantas have also been hauled up clasped tightly to an anchor chain. So powerful are these huge fish that a wounded manta, after being harpooned, has been known to tow a loaded 25-foot motorboat at cruising speed. As a rule, the huge manta is harmless, content to feed on a diet of shrimps and small fish. A PACIFIC MANTA, found off the southern California coast, is distinguished by white bars across the base of the pectoral fins and on the cephalic fins.

The Sawfish

Intermediate in body form between the rays and the sharks is the strange SAWFISH, an Atlantic fish common in the Gulf of Mexico and occasionally found as far north as New Jersey. The flattened body is widest at the head and bears broad but distinct pectoral fins; it is dark gray or brown with a yellowish or whitish underside. Most distinctive feature is an extension of the upper jaw into a long narrow blade whose edges are armed with stout peg-like teeth. The three-foot-long "saw" grows to a width of 9 inches at the base, with as many as 32 pairs of teeth along the edges of the blade. The unwieldy appendage is of no obvious advantage to the sawfish. Sawfish usually occur near shore in shallow water where they feed on small fishes; they are also found in brackish river mouths and among the bayous of the lower Mississippi River. A record specimen caught off Galveston, Texas, measured 16 feet in length and weighed 736 pounds.

Afterword:
Reference Books on Fishes

This has been only an introduction to the fishes of the United States. It has, I hope, whetted your curiosity so that you want to learn more about the species in your home lakes, streams, and oceanside. The number of books of a nontechnical nature that can add to your knowledge of fishes are unfortunately not very numerous. I have collected here as many as are available that will make a valuable addition to your nature library.

Field guides, essential for accurate identification of the species you encounter in a specific region, vary from those covering the entire country to those dealing with a single state. A standard classic is the *Field Book of Marine Fishes of the Atlantic Coast* by Charles M. Breder Jr., Curator of the Department of Fishes of the American Museum of Natural History in New York. It is published by G. P. Putnam's Sons. Another excellent general guide is *North American Game Fishes* by Francesca La Monte, also of the American Museum of Natural History. It is published by Doubleday and Company. *A Guide to Marine Fishes* by Alfred Perlmutter, published by New York University Press, deals with those species found in the mid-Atlantic states from Cap Cod to Virginia. *Fishes of the Great Lakes Region* by two well-known ichthyologists, Carl Hubbs and Karl Lagler, is a good guide to freshwater species of central and eastern United States. It is published by the Cranbrook Institute of Science, Bloomfield Hills, Michigan. In your own state or region, the state fish and wildlife organization can recommend pamphlets and bulletins dealing with native species of the region.

Libraries usually have copies of several large and out-of-print books on fishes that are valuable for reference. A classic is *The Fishes of North and Middle America* by David Starr Jordan and B. W. Evermann, Bulletin of the U.S. National Museum, No. 47, Parts I–IV, Washington, D.C. *The Fishes of the Gulf of Maine* by H. B. Bigelow and W. W. Welsh was published as a bulletin of the U.S. Bureau of Fisheries, Volume XL, Part 1. *The Fishes of Chesapeake Bay,* also a bulletin of the U.S. Bureau of Fisheries, Volume XLIII, was authored by S. F. Hildebrand and W. C. Schroeder. *Fishes of North Carolina* by H. M. Smith was published by the North Carolina Geological and Economic Survey.

The most abundant source of information on our freshwater and marine fishes is hidden away in the many excellent articles that have appeared in the *National Geographic Magazine,* the now defunct *Nature Magazine, Natural History,* and the various popular fish and wildlife magazines. The *Book of Fishes* incorporates many of the *National Geographic Magazine* articles of the past years in a single volume published by the National Geographic Society in Washington, D.C. For added information on the living habits of fishes, I can heartily recommend three books: *The Biology of Fishes,* by Harry M. Kyle, published in London by Sidgwick and Jackson; *The Ways of Fishes* by Leonard P. Schultz, Curator of Fishes at the U.S. National Museum, and Edith Stern, published by D. Van Nostrand Company of Princeton, New Jersey; and *Life Story of a Fish* by Brian Curtis, published by

D. Appleton-Century Company. The last named is a delightfully written and fascinating book. Much of interest about fishes and fishing in the North Atlantic is included in the excellent *Fish and Fisheries* by Sir Alister Hardy, a second volume of "The Open Sea: Its Natural History." It is published by Houghton Mifflin Company of Boston.

Index and List of Species Described in the Text

Every kind of fish has a scientific name as well as a common one. The advantage of the scientific name is that there is only one for each kind of fish, and each fish has only one such name. Fishes usually go by a bewildering variety of common names that not only vary from state to state, but from one river valley to another. In order to be sure of the exact kind of fish we are talking about, we must know the scientific name. Ichthyologists have cooperated to standardize both the common and scientific names of fishes, which is of great help in eliminating this confusion. The accompanying list uses the common and scientific names recommended by *A List of Common and Scientific Names of Fishes from the United States and Canada,* special publication No. 2 of the American Fisheries Society, second edition, 1960. Copies of this valuable aid to studying fishes can be secured for two dollars by writing to Secretary-Treasurer, American Fisheries Society, Box 483, McLean, Virginia.

Each species has a double scientific name indicating both the species and the genus to which it belongs. Atlantic salmon, for example, has the scientific name *Salmo salar;* the genus name (*Salmo*) comes first, the species name (*salar*) second. Species with the same genus name are close relatives. Since the scientific name of rainbow trout is *Salmo gairdneri*, we can expect that this fish has many of the features of the Atlantic salmon. Genera (the plural of genus) are grouped into families, thus placing related kinds of fishes together. The families in the accompanying list are in alphabetical order for reasons of simplicity. The letter "F" between the common and scientific names means that the species lives in freshwater habitats; the letter "A" means that it is a marine species restricted to the Atlantic Ocean; the letter "P" means that it is a marine species found only in the Pacific Ocean.

I. THE JAWLESS FISHES: *Class Agnatha*

LAMPREY FAMILY. *Petromyzontidae*

American Brook Lamprey	F	*Lampetra lamottei*	206
Sea Lamprey	A–F	*Petromyzon marinus*	206

II. THE CARTILAGINOUS FISHES: *Class Chondrichthyes*

DOGFISH SHARK FAMILY. *Squalidae*

Spiny Dogfish	A–P	*Squalus acanthias*	218
Greenland Shark	A	*Somniosus microcephalus*	219

ELECTRIC RAY FAMILY. *Torpedinidae*

Atlantic Torpedo	A	*Torpedo nobiliana*	221

HAMMERHEAD SHARK FAMILY. *Sphyrnidae*

Smooth Hammerhead	A–P	*Sphyrna zygaena*	211

MACKEREL SHARK FAMILY. *Lamnidae*

Basking Shark	A–P	*Cetorhinus maximus*	214
Bonito Shark	P	*Isurus glaucus*	212
Mako Shark	A	*Isurus oxyrinchus*	212
Porbeagle	A	*Lamna nasus*	212
White Shark	A–P	*Carcharodon carcharias*	214

MANTA FAMILY. *Mobulidae*

NURSE SHARK FAMILY. *Orectolobidae*

REQUIEM SHARK FAMILY. *Carcharhinidae*

SAND SHARK FAMILY. *Carchariidae*

SAWFISH FAMILY. *Pristidae*

SKATE FAMILY. *Rajidae*

STINGRAY FAMILY. *Dasyatidae*

THRESHER SHARK FAMILY. *Alopiidae*

WHALE SHARK FAMILY. *Rhincodontidae*

III. THE BONY FISHES: *Class Osteichthyes*

ANGLERFISH FAMILY. *Lophiidae*

BARRACUDA FAMILY. *Sphyraenidae*

Great Barracuda	A	*Sphyraena barracuda*	138
Northern Barracuda	A	*Sphyraena borealis*	139
Pacific Barracuda	P	*Sphyraena argentea*	139

BILLFISH FAMILY. *Istiophoridae*

Atlantic Sailfish	A	*Istiophorus albicans*	143
Blue Marlin	A	*Makaira nigricans*	143
Striped Marlin	P	*Makaira audax*	143
White Marlin	A	*Makaira albida*	143

BONEFISH FAMILY. *Albulidae*

Bonefish	A–P	*Albula vulpes*	140

BOWFIN FAMILY. *Amiidae.*

Bowfin	F	*Amia calva*	107

BLUEFISH FAMILY. *Pomatomidae*

Bluefish	A	*Pomatomus saltatrix*	128

BUTTERFLY FISH FAMILY. *Chaetodontidae*

Foureye Butterfly Fish	A	*Chaetodon capistratus*	172
Spotfin Butterfly Fish	A	*Chaetodon ocellatus*	172
French Angelfish	A	*Pomacanthus arcuatus*	172
Queen Angelfish	A	*Holacanthus ciliaris*	172
Rock Beauty	A	*Holacanthus tricolor*	174

CATFISH FAMILY (Freshwater Catfish). *Ictaluridae*

Blue Catfish	F	*Ictalurus furcatus*	78
Channel Catfish	F	*Ictalurus punctatus*	79
White Catfish	F	*Ictalurus catus*	80
Flathead Catfish	F	*Pylodictis olivaris*	78
Black Bullhead	F	*Ictalurus melas*	80
Brown Bullhead	F	*Ictalurus nebulosus*	80
Yellow Bullhead	F	*Ictalurus natalis*	80
Stonecat	F	*Noturus flavus*	80

CODFISH FAMILY. *Gadidae*

Burbot	F	*Lota lota*	158
Cod, Atlantic	A	*Gadus morhua*	154
Cusk	A	*Brosme brosme*	158

CODFISH FAMILY, *Gadidae (Cont.)*

Haddock	A	*Melanogrammus aeglefinus*	156
Hake, Pacific	P	*Merluccius productus*	157
Hake, Silver	A	*Merluccius bilinearis*	156
Hake, Squirrel	A	*Urophycis chuss*	158
Pollock	A	*Pollochius virens*	156
Tomcod, Atlantic	A	*Microgadus tomcod*	155
Tomcod, Pacific	P	*Microgadus proximus*	156

CUTLASSFISH FAMILY. *Trichiuridae*

Atlantic Cutlassfish	A	*Trichiurus lepturus*	195

DAMSELFISH FAMILY. *Pomacentridae*

Beau Gregory	A	*Eupomacentrus leucostictus*	174
Sergeant Major	A	*Abudefduf saxatilis*	174
Yellowtail Damselfish	A	*Microspathodon chrysurus*	174

DOLPHIN FAMILY. *Coryphaenidae*

Dolphin	A–P	*Coryphaena hippurus*	141

DRUM FAMILY. *Sciaenidae*

Croaker, Atlantic	A	*Micropogon undulatus*	120
Croaker, Black	P	*Cheilotrema saturnum*	120
Croaker, Spotfin	P	*Roncador stearnsi*	120
Croaker, Yellowfin	P	*Umbrina roncador*	120
Drum, Black	A	*Pogonias cromis*	117
Drum, Freshwater	F	*Aplodinotus grunniens*	119
Drum, Red	A	*Sciaenops ocellata*	119
Kingfish, California	P	*Menticirrhus undulatus*	122
Kingfish, Northern	A	*Menticirrhus saxatalis*	121
Kingfish, Southern	A	*Menticirrhus americanus*	122
Silver Perch	A	*Bairdiella chrysura*	121
Weakfish	A	*Cynoscion regalis*	121
White Sea-Bass	P	*Cynoscion nobilis*	120

EEL (FRESHWATER) FAMILY. *Anguillidae*

American Eel	A–F	*Anguilla rostrata*	102

FILEFISH FAMILY. *Balistidae*

Filefish, Orange	A	*Alutera schoepfi*	178
Filefish, Planehead	A	*Monacanthus hispidus*	178

FILEFISH FAMILY, *Balistidae* (*Cont.*)

Triggerfish, Common	A	*Balistes carolinensis*	176
Triggerfish, Queen	A	*Balistes vetula*	176

FROGFISH FAMILY. *Antennariidae*

Sargassum Fish	A	*Histrio histrio*	191

FLOUNDER (LEFTEYE) FAMILY. *Bothidae*

California Halibut	P	*Paralichthys californicus*	162
Summer Flounder	A	*Paralichthys dentatus*	160
Pacific Sand Dab	P	*Citharichthys sordidus*	159

FLOUNDER (RIGHTEYE) FAMILY. *Pleuronectidae*

Flounder, Starry	F–P	*Platichthys stellatus*	162
Flounder, Winter	A	*Pseudopleuronectes americanus*	160
Flounder, Witch	A	*Glyptocephalus cynoglossus*	160
Flounder, Yellowtail	A	*Limanda ferruginea*	160
Halibut, Atlantic	A	*Hippoglossus hippoglossus*	162
Halibut, Pacific	P	*Hippoglossus stenolepis*	162

FLYING-FISH FAMILY. *Exocoetidae*

Atlantic Flying Fish	A	*Cypselurus heterurus*	198
California Flying Fish	P	*Cypselurus californicus*	198

FLYING GURNARD FAMILY. *Dactylopteridae*

Flying Gurnard	A	*Dactylopterus volitans*	198

GAR FAMILY. *Lepisosteidae*

Alligator Gar	F	*Lepisosteus spatula*	106
Longnose Gar	F	*Lepisosteus osseus*	105

GREENLING FAMILY. *Hexagrammidae*

Kelp Greenling	P	*Hexagrammos decagrammus*	126
Lingcod	P	*Ophiodon elongatus*	126

GRUNT FAMILY. *Pomadasyidae*

Grunt, French	A	*Haemulon flavolineatum*	167
Grunt, White	A	*Haemulon plumieri*	167
Margate	A	*Haemulon album*	168
Margate, Black	A	*Anisotremus surinamensis*	168

GRUNT FAMILY, *Pomadasyidae (Cont.)*

Porkfish	A	*Anisotremus virginicus*	168
Pigfish	A	*Orthopristis chrysopterus*	168

HERRING FAMILY. *Clupeidae*

Alewife	A–F	*Alosa pseudoharengus*	150
American Shad	A–F–P	*Alosa sapidissima*	152
Atlantic Herring	A–P	*Clupea harengus*	149
Atlantic Menhaden	A	*Brevoortia tyrannus*	150
Spanish Sardine	A	*Sardinella anchovia*	150
Pacific Sardine	P	*Sardinops sagax*	150

JACK FAMILY. *Carangidae*

Amberjack, Greater	A	*Seriola dumerili*	136
Amberjack, Pacific	P	*Seriola colburni*	136
Banded Rudderfish	A	*Seriola zonata*	137
Blue Runner	A	*Caranx crysos*	136
Crevalle Jack	A	*Caranx hippos*	136
Lookdown	A	*Selene vomer*	137
Pilotfish	A–P	*Naucrates ductor*	137
Permit	A	*Trachinotus falcatus*	138
Pompano	A	*Trachinotus carolinus*	137

KILLIFISH FAMILY. *Cyprinodontidae*

Banded Killifish	F	*Fundulus diaphanus*	98
Blackstripe Topminnow	F	*Fundulus notatus*	98
Mummichog	A–F	*Fundulus heteroclitus*	98
Striped Killifish	A	*Fundulus majalis*	98

LIVE BEARER FAMILY. *Poeciliidae*

Mosquito Fish	A–F	*Gambusia affinis*	101

MACKEREL FAMILY. *Scombridae*

Albacore	A–P	*Thunnus alalunga*	131
Bonito, Atlantic	A	*Sarda sarda*	131
Mackerel, Atlantic	A	*Scomber scombrus*	129
Mackerel, Pacific	P	*Scomber japonicus*	131
Mackerel, Spanish	A	*Scomberomorus maculatus*	130
Tuna, Bluefin	A–P	*Thunnus thynnus*	132
Tuna, Yellowfin	A–P	*Thunnus albacares*	132
Tuna, Little	A	*Euthynnus alletteratus*	132
Wahoo	A	*Acanthocybium solanderi*	134

MINNOW FAMILY. *Cyprinidae*

Carp	F	*Cyprinus carpio*	96
Fallfish	F	*Semotilus corporalis*	96
Goldfish	F	*Carassius auratus*	97
Minnow, Cutlips	F	*Exoglossum maxillingua*	96
Minnow, Silvery	F	*Hybognathus nuchales*	94
Redside Dace	F	*Clinostomus elongatus*	94
Silver Shiner	F	*Notropis photogenis*	94
Sacramento Squawfish	F	*Ptychocheilus grandis*	96

MORAY EEL FAMILY. *Muraenidae*

Green Moray	A	*Gymnothorax funebris*	179
Spotted Moray	A	*Gymnothorax moringa*	179

MULLET FAMILY. *Mugilidae*

Striped Mullet	A–F–P	*Mugil cephalus*	134
White Mullet	A	*Mugil curema*	134

OARFISH FAMILY. *Regalecidae*

Oarfish	A–P	*Regalecus glesne*	196

OCEAN SUNFISH FAMILY. *Molidae*

Ocean Sunfish	A–P	*Mola mola*	200

PADDLEFISH FAMILY. *Polyodontidae*

Paddlefish	F	*Polyodon spathula*	109

PARROT FISH FAMILY. *Scaridae*

Blue Parrot Fish	A	*Scarus coeruleus*	171
Rainbow Parrot Fish	A	*Scarus guacamaia*	170

PERCH FAMILY. *Percidae*

Darter, Iowa	F	*Etheostoma exile*	89
Darter, Mud	F	*Etheostoma fusiforme*	89
Sauger	F	*Stizostedion canadense*	89
Walleye	F	*Stizostedion vitreum*	89
Yellow Perch	F	*Perca flavescens*	87

PIKE FAMILY. *Esocidae*

Muskellunge	F	*Esox masquinongy*	83
Pickerel, Chain	F	*Esox niger*	81

PIKE FAMILY, *Esocidae (Cont.)*

Pickerel, Redfin	F	*Esox americanus*	81
Pike, Northern	F	*Esox lucius*	81

PIPEFISH FAMILY. *Syngnathidae*

Pipefish, Dusky	A	*Syngnathus floridae*	202
Pipefish, Northern	A	*Syngnathus fuscus*	202
Sea Horse, Spotted	A	*Hippocampus erectus*	203

PORCUPINE-FISH FAMILY. *Diodontidae*

Porcupine Fish	A–P	*Diodon hystrix*	185
Striped Burrfish	A	*Chilomycterus schoepfi*	185

PORGY FAMILY. *Sparidae*

Porgy, Grass	A	*Calamus arctifrons*	123
Porgy, Northern (Scup)	A	*Stenotomus chrysops*	123
Sheepshead	A	*Archosargus probatocephalus*	123

PUFFER FAMILY. *Tetraodontidae*

Northern Puffer	A	*Sphaeroides maculatus*	184

REMORA (SHARK-SUCKER) FAMILY. *Echeneidae*

Shark-Sucker	A	*Echeneis naucrates*	200

SALMON (TROUT) FAMILY. *Salmonidae*

Cisco	F	*Coregonus artedii*	77
Salmon, Atlantic	A–F	*Salmo salar*	72
Salmon, Chinook (King)	F–P	*Oncorhynchus tshawytscha*	73
Salmon, Chum (Dog)	F–P	*Oncorhynchus keta*	73
Salmon, Coho (Silver)	A–F–P	*Oncorhynchus kisutch*	73
Salmon, Pink (Humpback)	A–F–P	*Oncorhynchus gorbuscha*	73
Salmon, Sockeye	F–P	*Oncorhynchus nerka*	73
Trout, Brown	A–F	*Salmo trutta*	76
Trout, Brook	A–F	*Salvelinus fontinalis*	77
Trout, Cutthroat	F–P	*Salmo clarki*	75
Trout, Dolly Varden	F–P	*Salvelinus malma*	77
Trout, Lake	F	*Salvelinus namaycush*	76
Trout, Rainbow	A–F–P	*Salmo gairdneri*	75
Whitefish, Lake	A–F	*Coregonus clupeaformis*	77

SCORPION FISH FAMILY. *Scorpaenidae*

Scorpion Fish	A	*Scorpaena plumeri*	187
Lion-fish	A	*Scorpaena grandicornis*	189

SCULPIN FAMILY. *Cottidae*

Cabezon	P	*Scorpaenichthys marmoratus*	190
Sculpin, Shorthorn	A–P	*Myoxocephalus scorpius*	190
Sculpin, Slimy	F	*Cottus cognatus*	190
Sea Raven	A	*Hemitripterus americanus*	190

SEA BASS FAMILY. *Serranidae*

Bass, Kelp	P	*Paralabrax clathratus*	114
Bass, Striped	A–F–P	*Roccus saxatilis*	113
Bass, White	F	*Roccus chrysops*	90
Bass, Yellow	F	*Roccus mississippiensis*	90
Grouper, Black	A	*Mycteroperca bonaci*	117
Grouper, Nassau	A	*Epinephelus striatus*	115
Grouper, Red	A	*Epinephelus morio*	115
Jewfish	A	*Epinephelus itajara*	117
Perch, White	A–F	*Roccus americanus*	90
Sea Bass, Black	A	*Centropristes striatus*	114
Sea Bass, Giant	P	*Stereolepis gigas*	115

SEA ROBIN FAMILY. *Triglidae*

Northern Sea Robin	A	*Prionotus carolinus*	189
Striped Sea Robin	A	*Prionotus evolans*	189

SMELT FAMILY. *Osmeridae*

American Smelt	A–F	*Osmerus mordax*	153

SNAPPER FAMILY. *Lutjanidae*

Muttonfish	A	*Lutjanus analis*	123
Snapper, Gray	A	*Lutjanus griseus*	122
Snapper, Red	A	*Lutjanus blackfordi*	122
Snapper, Vermilion	A	*Rhomboplites aurorubens*	122

SPADEFISH FAMILY. *Ephippidae*

Atlantic Spadefish	A	*Chaetodipterus faber*	171

SQUIRRELFISH FAMILY. *Holocentridae*

Squirrelfish	A	*Holocentrus ascensionis*	170